THE

MOSQUITOES

OF

BRITISH COLUMBIA

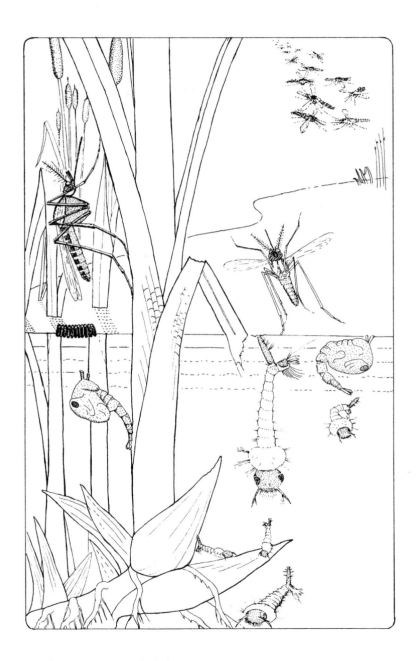

MOSQUITOES

"Indeed men from all countries agree that the musquitoes of B.C. are unmatched for numbers and ferocity."

—From Dr. Cheadle's description of the terrible "musquitoes" at the plains of Sumas in the Diary of his trip across British Columbia in 1863.

"There is nothing better to prevent the bad effects of mosquito bites than at once to dilute the liquid they have left in the wound with water. However small this wound may be, it will not be difficult for water to be introduced. By rubbing it will be at once enlarged, and there is nothing to do but wash it. I have sometimes found this remedy answer very well."

Réaumur, 1683–1757.

Frontispiece

Culex pipiens breeding and swarming over a lakeside pool with cattails.

BRITISH COLUMBIA PROVINCIAL MUSEUM

HANDBOOK No. 41

THE
MOSQUITOES
OF
BRITISH COLUMBIA

Written and Illustrated
by
Peter Belton

Province of British Columbia
Ministry of Provincial Secretary
and Government Services
Provincial Secretary

Published by the British Columbia Provincial Museum
Victoria

First Printing 1983

Canadian Cataloguing in Publication Data

Belton, Peter.
      The mosquitoes of British Columbia

      (Handbook / British Columbia Provincial Museum,
ISSN 0068-1628 ; no. 41)

      Bibliography: p.
      ISBN 0-7718-8359-5

      1. Mosquitoes - British Columbia - Identification.
I. British Columbia Provincial Museum.   II. Title.
III. Series: Handbook (British Columbia Provincial
Museum) ; no. 41.

QL536.B44   595.77'1   C83-092116-8

PREFACE

This handbook has the same objectives as the earlier Occasional Paper, *The Mosquitoes of British Columbia* (Curtis 1967a), namely to assist those interested in the biology and identity of our mosquito fauna.

Curtis' keys (with the author's approval, given before his death in 1979) were used as a starting point for this book. They, and the descriptions of individual species have been extensively revised and line drawings of larvae and of some of the more important adult characters have been added.

For those concerned with mosquito management it is essential to identify the larvae, particularly if chemical control techniques are to be used efficiently. Diagrams of larvae are therefore included so that characters, besides those used in the keys, can be compared. I have referred to other publications that illustrate the females and genitalia of the males.

The descriptions indicate that some species can be identified rather easily whereas others, in which particular characters vary from one specimen to another, will present difficulties even to expert taxonomists with the best of equipment. In some cases adults will have to be reared from larvae because characters of larvae and of both sexes of adults may be needed to make identification certain.

The enthusiasm of Dr. D. M. Wood (Biosystematics Research Institute, Ottawa) was the spark mainly responsible for starting me on this endeavour but its completion would not have been possible without the cooperation, encouragement and assistance of my wife who wrote the chapter on history, typed the manuscript and did most of the unexciting routines of writing such as indexing, etc. My family also assisted on numerous collecting expeditions, sometimes actively, sometimes as bait.

Many colleagues contributed ideas, read portions of the manuscript, tested the keys and allowed me to look at collections. These include Dr. G. E. Scudder (University of British Columbia), Dr. R. A. Costello (B.C. Ministry of Agriculture and Food), Dr. H. R. McCarthy (Simon Fraser University), Dr. R. A. Ellis (Parks and Recreation Department, Winnipeg), Dr. R. Vockeroth (Biosystematics Research Institute, Ottawa) and Dr. G. Pritchard and P. Schofield (University of Calgary).

Special thanks are due to Dr. G. Steyskal, until recently of the Smithsonian Institute, Washington, for translating many of the Greek names and for improving my translation of some of the Latin ones. I also wish to acknowledge the editorial comments and helpful criticisms of Dr. R. A. Cannings and Harold Hosford of the British Columbia Provincial Museum.

Finally, I am most grateful to R. Yorke Edwards, Director of the Museum, for his support and to several former chairmen, deans and presidents of Simon Fraser University who approved a study of the Province's mosquitoes as a subject for my sabbatical leave in 1977.

P. Belton
September, 1982

CONTENTS

LIST OF FIGURES

11

LIST OF TABLES

INTRODUCTION

BIOLOGY

Mosquitoes belong to one of the largest insect orders, the Diptera or true (two-winged) flies. This order has about 67 families. The one to which the mosquitoes belong is called the Culicidae. Some authorities divide the Culicidae into three subfamilies, the Culicinae, or biting mosquitoes, and the Dixiinae and Chaoborinae which are non-biting. Most taxonomists now restrict the family Culicidae to the biting species and place the dixids and chaoborids in separate families, as I do. There are five genera of Culicidae found in British Columbia, *Aedes, Anopheles, Culex, Culiseta* and *Mansonia*. They can easily be identified in the adult stage as the only flies with a long proboscis, long antennae and scaled wings. The larvae of all three families are aquatic. Most mosquito larvae have a respiratory siphon but the anophelines (species of *Anopheles*), dixids, and some chaoborids do not. Characters to separate the siphonless larvae are given later in the description of the genus *Anopheles*. Mosquitoes pass through four stages—egg, larva, pupa, adult. The eggs hatch into larvae which, as they feed, outgrow their skins. These are moulted three times as the larvae increase in size from first instar to fully grown fourth instar. These then moult to become the pupae, from which the adults emerge.

There are two enormous advantages attached to the study of biting insects. First the insects, at least the adult females, do the searching. All the collector need do is expose him or herself, with suitable equipment, to collect undamaged specimens. Secondly, none of the biting species of mosquito could be described as endangered. On the whole they are adapted to breed in sites where there are few predators or to emerge from their larval sites before the population of predators can build up to deal with them (James 1961). In other words, they are pests.

As mentioned in the Preface, the identification of some species of mosquitoes, particularly if only biting females are collected, is extremely difficult even for the expert. However, if the larvae and both sexes of the adults that develop from them are available, any species can be identified with confidence.

Collection should therefore be started early in the year with a tour of larval breeding sites. Table I shows some of the obvious differences

15

between the genera and Table II gives the collector a rough timetable to follow.

Overwintering females of *Anopheles, Culex* and most species of *Culiseta* can be collected from their hibernation sites between November and February or March. The greatest numbers, however, are found on the wing in spring and fall, just after and just before hibernation. Some of the *Culiseta* are known as snow mosquitoes because the females often emerge from hibernation on warm days when snow is still on the ground. Adults of most aedines (species of *Aedes*) are abundant in the summer, from late May to July, then become scarcer and die off in the fall after laying their eggs. These are laid in crevices or on vegetation in spots that will not be flooded until the following spring. The eggs of some aedines will not hatch until they have undergone a period of drying and chilling. In some species, some of the eggs do not hatch after the first flooding but produce larvae only after the second or even third summer. In the Lower Mainland, the first larvae of *Aedes* can usually be found in February. Most aedines have only one generation a year but late-hatching larvae can be found until June and July at higher altitudes and latitudes. Aedines that develop in the rot cavities of trees (tree-hole mosquitoes) and in pools in coastal rock may overwinter as larvae.

The eggs of *Anopheles, Culex* and most species of *Culiseta* are laid on the surface of water, singly by anophelines but in rafts by *Culex* and *Culiseta*. These eggs hatch within a few days. The first larvae usually appear in March and April in the Lower Mainland. Eggs, larvae and pupae can be found throughout the summer because most species of these genera can produce several generations in a season, depending on the temperature and rainfall.

Eggs of *Mansonia* are laid on vegetation or in rafts on the surface of water. On hatching, the larvae dive and attach themselves to the underwater stems or roots of plants where they overwinter.

In general, male mosquitoes can be distinguished from females by the abundance of long setae on their antennae which give them a characteristically bushy appearance. In addition, most males have palps about as long as the proboscis; this is also true, however, of female anophelines. Males are usually smaller than females of the same species and emerge one or two days earlier. This is probably because the male larvae do not have to feed more to store food reserves for egg production. Females must make this extra effort, and so pupate and emerge after the male larvae.

TABLE I
Generic differences visible to the naked eye or with a hand lens.

	ANOPHELES	AEDES	CULEX & CULISETA

EGG

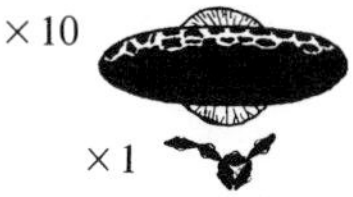

× 10

× 1

Eggs laid singly
on water
float horizontally
buoyant lateral wings

Eggs single or in
clusters on substrate
non-floating

Eggs laid in rafts on water
float vertically

LARVA

at surface

dorsal view

horizontal at surface
no siphon

These larvae could
be either AEDES or CULEX

hang from surface
well-developed siphon

PUPA

ADULT

head of AEDES
or CULEX

head of female

palps same length
as proboscis

palps much shorter
than proboscis

**TIP OF
ABDOMEN**

rounded

♂   ♂

ceri   gonocoxites
pointed   large

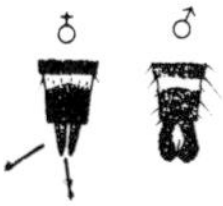

♂   ♂

blunt   small

**RESTING
POSITION**

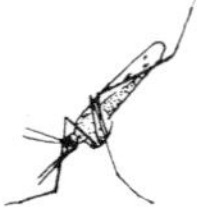

17

TABLE II

Approximate times and durations of the life stages of mosquitoes in British Columbia.

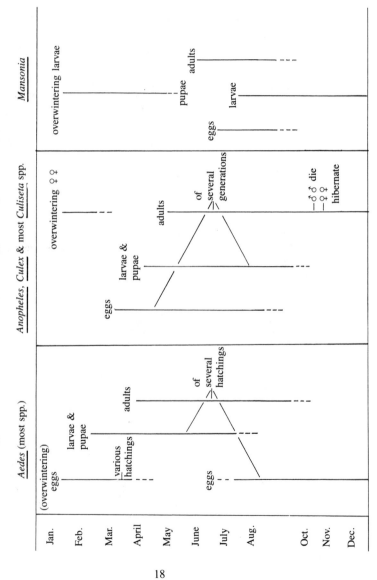

Adult males do not live as long as the females and appear to die soon after mating even in species in which the females hibernate. Both sexes probably feed on nectar after emergence to obtain enough nutrients for flight. Mating usually occurs in swarms, at dusk and dawn. Males congregate at "swarm sites" and females are somehow attracted to them. The females fly up into the swarm where the sound of their wings beating (100–400 times/sec.) is detected by the "bottlebrush" antennae of the males. The first male to arrive clasps the female and they drop out of the swarm. The male usually deposits a packet of sperm in the female before the pair reach the ground and the male rejoins the swarm while the female flies off. Females now require protein to mature their eggs and, in most species, begin to search for a source of blood. The search seems to be triggered by an increase in the level of carbon dioxide in the air. This usually means that an animal is nearby. This, and other clues, such as heat and moisture, lead the female closer to her host. In many species the initiation of mating, feeding and oviposition is controlled by an internal clock that switches on at dusk and dawn even when the insects are kept in complete darkness (Jones and Gubbins 1978).

In a few species, females can mature eggs without a blood meal and, in some of these, the wing muscles are broken down to provide protein. Such mosquitoes are termed autogenous but some of them mature additional broods of eggs if they can obtain blood. Other species feed on birds, reptiles or amphibians even if mammals are available. These and the autogenous species are seldom pests.

Mosquitoes are considered to be pests when they bite humans or domestic animals, mostly because of the irritation produced but sometimes because they transmit, or vector, diseases from one host to another. Fortunately, few mosquito-borne diseases occur in British Columbia although one of them, Western Equine Encephalitis (WEE), caused by a virus, can damage the nervous system. As its name implies, WEE is usually restricted to horses which are immunised against the virus in the western provinces. California Encephalitis, another viral disease, has been found in small mammals in many parts of Canada. Our particular strain, however, does not appear to produce any symptoms. Malaria, the most widespread human disease vectored by mosquitoes, was formerly endemic in the northwestern part of the continent. So far as I am aware there has never been an epidemic in British Columbia. Most cases reported nowadays in Canada have been 'imported' from regions where, once almost eliminated, malaria is unfortunately becoming all too common again.

Adult mosquitoes may perform one useful function, namely pollinating the flowers they visit. This behaviour is particularly obvious in the case of orchids which have sticky pollenia. Mosquitoes, especially in the north, are sometimes found with these pollenia attached to their heads, elsewhere they can be found with a dusting of pollen.

MOSQUITOES IN THE CULTURE OF NORTHWEST COAST INDIANS

Several legends describe the origin of mosquitoes (Outram 1973). According to the Alaskan Tlingits, mosquitoes came from a 16-foot cannibal, Goo-teekhl, who was trapped and burned by members of the Frog House. The sparks from his ashes turned into clouds of mosquitoes.

The Kwakiutl legend is told around an ancestor of chief Wa-kias of Alert Bay. Wa-kias had the story carved on his housepole in 1899 and the pole was painted *in situ* by Emily Carr, then moved to Vancouver and erected in Stanley Park in 1927 (Raley 1937). The fourth crest from the top of the pole represents this ancestor, Nan-wa-kawie, the wise one, who, with his four sons, killed a family of cannibal giants from Forbidden Valley. The sons were hunting mountain goat in the valley and, despite their father's warning, visited the giants. They escaped with the aid of four magical articles that delayed the giant's pursuit. Nan-wa-kawie was forced to bargain for the lives of his sons. He invited the giant with his wife and son to a feast. During the preparations, Nan-wa-kawie's slaves dug a deep pit near the fire and balanced a settee over it. The chief lulled the giants to sleep on the settee and then they were tipped into the pit and killed by throwing in boiling water and red-hot stones. As Nan-wa-kawie scattered the ashes to the winds, saying "You shall pursue men for all time in all places," they turned into mosquitoes and other biting insects.

In Tsimshian mythology the body of a chief, who had a crystal proboscis, was burned and his ashes, when blown on, flew upwards and became mosquitoes (Stewart 1979).

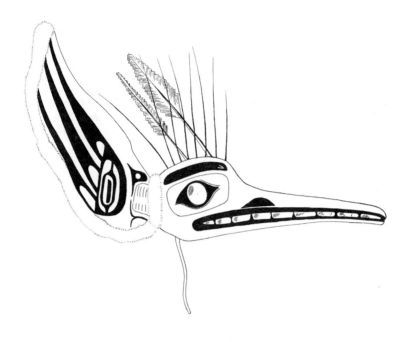

Fig. 1.   Coastal Indian mask representing a mosquito.

The Haida myth involves a young girl who broke her seclusion taboos and went to play with her brothers. Huge-Belly, a monster of the mountains, appeared and used his long, shiny, knife-like nose to split open most of the law-breakers and hung them in the rafters of his smoke house. The guilty young woman and one of her brothers escaped and hid in some trees by a lake where Huge-Belly's sister found them. Pouncing on them with the characteristic poor aim of Indian monsters, she plunged into the freezing lake and cried "The people shall always suffer the sting of my nose." The survivors then adopted the crest of Weelaek, the mosquito, for their clan (Barbeau 1957).

The Weelaek crest is carved on a totem pole at Fort Simpson. A similar crest, with a two-metre nose, is at the bottom of a pole at Gitliks. A cannibal mosquito is shown on one side of an argillite chest now in the National Museum of Canada (Barbeau 1957, Fig. 63), and the Tlingit cannibal or mosquito is carved on a housepost at Klukwan, Alaska (Barbeau 1953, Fig. 194).

Mosquitoes have also been carved on masks and ladles. One of the older masks has a long proboscis inlaid with teeth of haliotis shell, leather wings fringed with eagle down, and walrus whiskers decorating the head (Fig. 1). It was collected from Indians on the northwest coast by the Russian explorer Voznesensky in the 1840s and is now in the museum in Leningrad (Siebert and Forman 1969).

More recently, Stewart (1979) illustrates a print of a mosquito by a contemporary artist from 'Ksan.

HISTORY

by E. M. Belton

Before the arrival of Captain Cook and the early white settlers, the vast area of British Columbia was ideally suited to the production of immense hordes of mosquitoes and other biting flies. Probably the first published reference to mosquitoes in British Columbia was in Simon Fraser's diary in 1808 (Lamb 1960). As his dugouts emerged from the Fraser canyon into the lower reaches of the river, he wrote "Musketoes are in clouds . . ." Since the early 1900s, however, many of the breeding areas, particularly in and around towns and cities, have been eliminated or their mosquitoes controlled. Most residents have no idea what a pestilence mosquitoes used to be or even what they still are like in remote areas of the Province. Early settlers told of dogs and calves being killed by mosquitoes and (although it sounds unlikely) of a cow whose tail was so bitten that it dropped off (Crosby 1907).

The first collections of mosquitoes in the Province were made in the lower Fraser Valley in the 1850s. Scientific studies were begun in the early 1900s by J. Fletcher, R. C. Treherne and C. G. Hewitt of the then Dominion Entomological Branch. They made surveys at various times and submitted specimens for identification to H. G. Dyar of the United States National Museum, the leading North American mosquito taxonomist. Dyar, himself, visited the Kootenays in 1904 and Vancouver Island in 1906. In 1919 he collected mosquitoes from Prince George to the coast along the line of the Canadian National Railway, and at White Pass and Bennett, on the way to the Yukon. In 1920 he visited the Fraser Valley. Subsequently he published *The Mosquitoes of British Columbia and the Yukon Territory, Canada* (Dyar 1920) with descriptions of about 25 species, their localities and notes on their life histories.

As immigration increased, so did logging, farming and building. In the Fraser Valley demands for relief from the mosquito pestilence also increased. The National Research Council, in co-operation with the Dominion Department of Agriculture, set up a project to study the problem. Eric Hearle was hired to work in the Valley in the summers of 1919, 1920 and 1921 and a laboratory was established at Mission, the worst mosquito-infested area. From this centre, Hearle studied the problem and in 1919 he made what was probably the first aerial entomological survey in Canada when he flew over Chilliwack, Sumas and Nicomen and photographed mosquito breeding sites. A much wider survey was made in 1921 when aerial photographs were taken of a 2,000 square mile area between Hope and Vancouver on May 28 when the flood level reached 17' 6'' and on June 12 when it peaked at 21' 4'' (Hearle 1922). His report, *The Mosquitoes of the Lower Fraser Valley, British Columbia, and Their Control*, was published in 1926 and gives an interesting picture of what life was like then. A table shows the levels of the Fraser at the Mission bridge from 1910–1921 and how the height of the spring flood affected the seriousness of the mosquito scourge later in the year. His recommendations for their control are discussed later. Twenty-three species of mosquitoes were collected in the Valley. Some interesting changes in their abundance have occurred since and these are also mentioned later. In 1927 Hearle published a list of mosquitoes and locality records for the entire Province. Three of the 42 species he listed are not now regarded as true species, leaving a total of 39.

From 1922–1925 Hearle investigated the mosquitoes of Rocky Mountain National Park, Alberta, and organised successful control programs in the area. In 1926 he moved to Saskatchewan but returned to British Columbia in 1928 and helped to establish the Dominion Insect Laboratory at Kamloops. He became its officer-in-charge and surveyed the biting flies, ticks, mites and lice of the southern half of the Province. By 1930 he had set up mosquito control programs at Kamloops and Kelowna. At the invitation of the Canadian National Railway, he spent the summers of 1931 and 1932 surveying the mosquito problem in Jasper National Park. Following this work his health broke down (it had not been good since he was injured in World War I) and he was an invalid until his death in 1934 at the age of 41.

From 1926–1941 Dr. A. Gibson, the Dominion Entomologist, gave annual accounts of mosquito-suppression work in British Columbia and the rest of Canada, at the annual meetings of the New Jersey Mosquito Extermination Association. As a result of abnormally high spring floods which spread over areas of dense cottonwood, 1932 was an exceptionally bad mosquito year in British Columbia. In his account of the season, Gibson reported that although mosquito control operations in and around Kamloops kept the city fairly free of the pest, only 15 miles away, haying had to be stopped because tormenting mosquitoes made the horses unmanageable. He also quoted newspaper accounts describing the lower North Thomson Valley where so many smudges were burning that the countryside looked as if it was on fire. In his account of mosquito supression in 1934, he described strawberry pickers at Telegraph Bay on Vancouver Island driven from the fields by hordes of mosquitoes which had flown over a high ridge from the tidal marsh where they were breeding. He also described how staff at Tranquille Sanatorium near Kamloops had to run when they moved from one building to another, until control measures were undertaken.

Following Hearle's death in 1934, Prof. G. J. Spencer from the University of British Columbia took charge of the Kamloops Laboratory during the summer months until G. Allen Mail became officer-in-charge in 1937. Mail had been Hearle's assistant in the Rocky Mountain Park investigations but then went to Montana where he published the comprehensive booklet, *The Mosquitoes of Montana*, in 1934. The Kamloops laboratory was now in larger quarters and much work was done on mosquito control techniques and on testing mosquito repellents. Mail returned to the United States in 1943 and J. D. Gregson took over. Gregson later became internationally known for his work on tick-borne paralysis.

In 1949, a Household and Medical Entomology Unit was established at the Kamloops laboratory and L. C. Curtis became officer-in-charge.

The Livestock Insect Section closed in 1971. Today assessment of mosquito problems and research is done by the Provincial Ministries of Agriculture and Environment with some research going on at the University of British Columbia, Simon Fraser University and the University of Victoria.

Most species of mosquitoes identified from the Province are now in the Canadian National Collection in Ottawa, to which the Kamloops material was transferred. Small reference collections are kept by the Ministry of Agriculture and Food Laboratory at Cloverdale, in the G. J. Spencer Collection at the University of British Columbia, at Simon Fraser University and at the Provincial Museum, Victoria.

In 1967 Curtis published the first comprehensive account of the mosquitoes of British Columbia in an Occasional Paper of the British Columbia Provincial Museum entitled *The Mosquitoes of British Columbia*. He described 42 species from the Province and included 5 more species that might be expected to occur.

Since then, two species new to Canada, *Aedes togoi* and *Ae.* nevadensis*, have been found in British Columbia and another, *Ae. schizopinax*, just across the border, on the Alberta side of the Rocky Mountain foothills. Four resurrected specific names, *Ae. aloponotum*, *Ae. euedes*, *Ae. mercurator* and *Ae. provocans* have been shown to apply to mosquitoes already present in the Province and one species, *Ae. hendersoni* was misidentified as *Ae. triseriatus* (Wood *et al.* 1979). Of the five species that Curtis expected would later be found in the Province, two, *Ae. melanimon* and *Culiseta minnesotae*, have now been collected, bringing the total number of species of mosquitoes recorded in the Province to 46.

LIFE ZONES

Compared with the other provinces, British Columbia has a rich mosquito fauna. To some extent, this is because we have species that only occur west of the Rocky Mountain barrier but it probably also reflects the varied life zones, from desert to rain forests, that occur in the Province.

---

* Abbreviations used for genera are: *Aedes, Ae.; Anopheles, An.; Culex, Cx.; Culiseta, Cs.; Mansonia, Ma.* (Reinert 1975).

The least mobile life forms show the greatest discrimination between biotic areas or zones and, in fact, such zones are usually based on the distribution of plants. Mosquitoes, like dragonflies (Cannings and Stuart 1977) can fly, or may be blown, long distances so that specific habitats, or microzones, suitable for their immature stages, are often more important to them than the larger life zones that affect the distribution of mammals. Some species, like *Ae. cinereus, Ae. sticticus* and *An. earlei* have been recorded from every zone. Others, like *Ae. cataphylla, Ae. vexans, Cx. territans* and *Cs. alaskaensis* may prove to be almost as widespread. Nevertheless, some mosquitoes are specialized to breed in particular habitats, for example, in alkaline pools which are only found in areas where the salty, ground-water seepage exceeds the rainfall. This occurs in dry forest and more arid zones. Thirteen biotic areas are recognized in the Province (Munro and Cowan 1947). These can be grouped into the following six life zones which have distinct mosquito faunas (Fig. 2).

Osoyoos Arid Zone

Water is scarce here but there are many mosquitoes to be found. Little breeding occurs in permanent lakes and rivers unless they contain weedy backwaters or floodplains. In such habitats *An. freeborni, Ae. vexans, Ae. spencerii, Ae. dorsalis, Ae. melanimon, Cs. inornata* and *Cx. tarsalis* are found. Irrigation in this and the Dry Forest Zone provides an ideal habitat for many of these species, particularly if cattle or horses graze nearby. *Ae. dorsalis* and *Ae. melanimon* can tolerate a considerable degree of salinity and large numbers of their larvae are found in saline pools in this and the Parkland Zones.

Dry Forest Zone

Most of the species of the previous zone are found here. *Ae. campestris* is locally more abundant than *Ae. dorsalis* in the Kamloops and Shuswap areas and *Ae. flavescens*, a species commonly associated with them, is also found in the north of this zone. Timbered floodplains along rivers yield *Ae. increpitus* and *Ae. sticticus* although these species are commoner in more luxuriantly forested areas. There is also one tree-hole species, *Ae. hendersoni*, found in this and the Columbia Forest Zone. It has not been found west of the Cascade Mountains.

Fig. 2.   Biotic areas of British Columbia (after Munro and Cowan 1947).

27

Cariboo and Peace River Parkland Zones

Prairie species like *Ae. flavescens* and *Ae. campestris* are found here in open saline pools, along with the more widespread *Ae. cataphylla* and *Ae. mercurator*. In the past, adults of the latter may have been confused with *Ae. euedes* which is also found in the Cariboo area. *Ae. riparius* has not been found west of the Rocky Mountains. Widely distributed in the prairies, *riparius* is found in this zone and in northern boreal forest in British Columbia. Frequently associated with it in the prairies and restricted to this zone in our Province, is the pale form of *Ae. spencerii*. Another prairie species, *Ae. nigromaculis*, has been found on the Alberta side of the border in this zone and will probably ultimately be found in British Columbia.

Columbia Forest Zone

Many of the species in this zone are also found in coastal forest. *Ae. communis*, one of the species breeding in woodland pools, has so far been recorded from the Columbia Forest, Boreal Forest, and northern Coastal Forest. *Ma. perturbans* and *Cs. morsitans*, species of permanent swamps, have been recorded from this zone and, more generally, in the south of the Coastal Forest. Our two species breeding in tree-holes, *Ae. hendersoni* and *Ae. sierrensis*, overlap here and this appears to be the eastern limit of the latter's range.

Alplands, Subalpine and Boreal Forest Zones

Few collections have been made in these zones. Captures were made by Dyar (1920) in the boreal forest around Teslin and Atlin, by the Northern Insect Survey (Freeman 1952) at Lower Post and Muncho L., and by Hearle (1932) in the Subalpine Zone of the Rocky Mountains. *Ae. impiger* and *Ae. nigripes*, characteristic of the Rocky Mountain subalpine, are also found farther north in the arctic tundra. Hearle also found *Cs. alaskaensis* and *Ae. pullatus* which can be found in other zones at lower elevations. Dyar found that *Ae. communis* was the most abundant snow-melt mosquito in the boreal forest, followed by *Ae. cataphylla* and *Ae. hexodontus*. *Ae. pionips* was less common and *Ae. implicatus* was found in dense woodland. Dyar did not separate the banded-leg mosquitoes he found here. He thought they were a complex of *Ae. fitchii*, *Ae. excrucians* and *Ae. mercurator*. The complex may also have contained

Ae. euedes. I have found *Ae. hexodontus* in Subalpine and Alpine Zones across the south of the Province in the Coast, Cascade and Rocky Mountains.

Coast Forest, Puget Sound Lowlands and Island Zones

In the wet forests of the Lower Mainland and Vancouver Island, *Ae. aloponotum* reaches the northern limit of its distribution along the west coast of North America. *Ae. aboriginis* has a similar coastal distribution but extends into Alaska. *Cs. minnesotae*, although widely distributed in North America has only been found in this zone in British Columbia. It will probably be found elsewhere in the Province, having only recently been recognized as a species distinct from *Cs. morsitans. An. punctipennis* is widely distributed in this zone. It has a very peculiar distribution in North America, occurring in every province except Alberta and Saskatchewan. Despite systematic collecting, it has not been found between the Chilcotin and Manitoba. One species, *Cx. pipiens*, was accidentally introduced into the Lower Mainland early in the twentieth century. It has now spread along the south of the Province into the dry interior. Another possible introduction, *Ae. togoi*, is restricted to coastal rock-pools and is therefore found only in coastal zones. It was first discovered on the Saanich Peninsula, Vancouver Island, in 1969. Since then it has been collected from localities between Mittelnatch Island and South Pender Island. *Ae. dorsalis* which is found in saline pools in the dry interior, is also found in coastal salt marshes in this zone, from Nanaimo and the Sechelt Peninsula south to California. There seem to be no species unique to the Gulf Islands and Puget Sound Lowlands. Both coastal and woodland habitats appear to support the same mosquito fauna as those of the southern Coastal Forest. Little is known of the mosquitoes of the Queen Charlotte Islands.

MANAGEMENT

Apart from a few legends mentioned earlier, we have little evidence of how mosquitoes interacted with the original inhabitants of British Columbia but one suspects that the native people must have built their villages at a respectable distance from the worst mosquito breeding sites. Lord (1866) noted that on Sumas Lake the summer lodges of local Indians were built on piles far from the shore. The Indians probably relied on smoke and perhaps also animal fat and fish oil as "repellents". Also, because some species of mosquitoes do not enter buildings, the people probably went indoors in the evening when the mosquitoes were at their worst. Contemporary prints show portages where the canoeists were wearing squares of loosely woven material over their heads, although these may have been for protection against black flies rather than mosquitoes.

The experiences of pioneer white travellers and settlers is well documented (Curtis 1967a). At least until the 1930s, they screened their houses, sprayed the inside of buildings with creosote and applied repellents to exposed parts of the body. Interestingly enough, two of the repellents advocated at the turn of the century, oils of lemon grass (citronella) and lavender, are still registered as insect repellents by the Federal Department of Agriculture.

The first organized mosquito control in the Province was initiated by a memorandum from two federal and one provincial entomologist to the Minister of Agriculture (Cameron *et al.* 1917). This far-sighted document recommended treating breeding sites with oil or larvicides for temporary relief and, for more permanent control, the drainage or cleaning and deepening of the margins of swampy areas and salt marshes. They noted that stocking permanent bodies of water with small fish had also been successful and indicated the need for a complete survey of the lower Fraser Valley and a study of the habits of each species of mosquito. This recommendation resulted in the appointment of Mr. Eric Hearle as described earlier.

Hearle's studies and his publication of *The Mosquitoes of the Lower Fraser Valley, British Columbia, and Their Control* (1926), led to the virtual clearance of mosquitoes from large areas of the Valley by eliminating their breeding places. This was achieved by drainage and filling or, in large flood-plains, by dyking and pumping. Following the completion of the Sumas dyke, more than half of the flood-water breeding area in the lower Fraser Valley was reclaimed and Sumas residents noticed an "extraordinary reduction in the mosquito pest in that district" (Hearle 1927b). Many of the dykes and drainage canals, including those at Sumas, Hatzic and Langley are still used.

The Dominion Department of Agriculture recommended such methods in the bulletin *Mosquito Control In Canada* (Hearle & Twinn 1928). They also suggested controlling water levels to prevent flooding during the spring run-off and deepening and cleaning the margins of shallow temporary pools to improve the effectiveness of natural enemies and the stirring action of wind. More importantly, they recognized the need to identify and avoid treating areas of standing water that yielded no mosquitoes. This advice can hardly be bettered today, although there is now more concern over the preservation of wetlands.* Other methods of control, which were recognized as temporary, included the application of a light petroleum oil (furnace fuel) to standing water with a hand- or pump-sprayer and, where there was a lot of vegetation, by spreading sawdust soaked in oil to kill larvae and pupae. A small quantity of kerosene or a pound of lime was recommended to prevent mosquitoes from breeding in water barrels. Details of how to set up a community mosquito control program, survey potential breeding sites, and carry out the control measures, were given.

Several tests of biological control methods were carried out in the 1920s. The effectiveness of different species of fish as predators of mosquito larvae had been investigated, off and on, at least since the 1890s (Howard 1900) and in 1924 the mosquito-eating fish, *Gambusia affinis,* was imported from California and released at Banff, Alberta, where it is still reported to occur in warm sulphur pools. An attempt, in 1929, to establish the fish in a deep pond on the golf course in Kelowna failed, however, because none survived the winter even though the pond did not freeze to the bottom (West 1963).

Oil films, which prevent mosquito larvae and pupae from surfacing to obtain air, were widely used as a means of control in southern British Columbia from 1920 or thereabouts. This treatment was often effective; for example, in 1930, G. C. Nott, in charge of control for the city of Kamloops, reduced the adult population to "practically non-existent throughout the season" with a budget of $600. On the other hand, also in 1930, this technique did not control mosquitoes in Eagle Valley, between Revelstoke and Sicamous, apparently because old engine oil, which presumably did not produce an even film, was used (Gibson 1931).

Mosquito Control In Canada was not revised until World War II (Twinn 1941) when the staff of the Kamloops laboratory, under Allen Mail's direction, evaluated techniques for power spraying and the use of

---

* The current provincial Mosquito Control Guide (B.C. Mosquito Advisory Committee 1981) requires approval of the Ministry of Environment before sensitive areas with resident wildlife can be drained.

derris (rotenone) to protect livestock. They also carried out research for the armed forces on the effectiveness of new mosquito repellents. At this time, the general public was advised to use a coal tar disinfectant, as an alternative to oil, for killing larvae and, for the first time, pyrethrin fly sprays were recommended for killing adults. In that bulletin, the first mention is made of pyrethrin as a potent additive to personal repellents. This discovery, made by "Scotty" McNay, was evidently forgotten for 35 years but interest has now revived in the use of very powerful synthetic pyrethrins as repellents on loosely woven jackets and hoods (Lindsay & McAndless 1978).

Recommendations for mosquito control in Canada were next revised by Twinn & Peterson (1955). At that time, the inexpensive and effective insecticide DDT, was widely advocated. Nevertheless, Twinn & Peterson emphasized elimination or reduction of breeding sites to achieve permanent control. If this was not feasible, they recommended the use of DDT and related organochlorides. Of course, nothing was then known of the harmful effects on the environment of these almost indestructible compounds. Insect screens and new synthetic repellents such as dimethyl phthallate (DMP) and Rutgers 612 were suggested to ward off adult mosquitoes, with a note that these repellents are effective for much longer periods when applied to the outside of clothing rather than to the body.

By 1967 the adverse effects of DDT were well known and although its use was still recommended by the Canada Department of Agriculture, restrictions were noted in L. C. Curtis's booklet, *How To Wage A Mosquito Control Campaign*. He recommended the new synthetic repellent, diethyl toluamide, for personal protection. This substance, better known under the trade name Off®, is still one of the most effective mosquito repellents.

The most recent recommendations of the Federal Government (Agriculture Canada 1972) do not refer to specific insecticides. Several provinces now publish their own recommendations. These are revised whenever insecticides, or their rates of application, are changed.

British Columbia has always been one of the leaders in environmental consciousness and suggested in its *Mosquito Control Guides* the possibility of using fish to control mosquitoes, despite their early failure in Kelowna. The current Provincial Guide is available, free, from the Publications Office of the Ministry of Agriculture, Legislative Buildings, Victoria, or from Regional Offices.

Other promising techniques that are being investigated in the Province include the use of substances for regulating the growth of insects (some of which are now registered pesticides), selectively toxic bacteria, algae and plants, parasitic nematode worms and insect predators of mosquito larvae. Other techniques such as the release of sterile male mosquitoes or of mosquitoes that are genetically or cytoplasmically incompatible with native species, and the use of attractants to trap large numbers of mosquitoes, or their eggs, are also being investigated but may require several more years of research and apply only to some of our major pests.

COLLECTING AND PRESERVING

Adults

The easiest way to collect the females of biting mosquitoes is to trap them in a plastic vial when they have settled on an exposed arm or leg. The vial is placed over the mosquito and the lid slipped under the vial when the mosquito flies up. If the specimens are not required alive they can be trapped in a glass killing tube (Fig. 3). Cut up enough rubber bands to make a 5 mm layer in the bottom of the tube. Cover the rubber with chloroform and insert the stopper. Leave the tube for several minutes until the rubber swells and absorbs all the chloroform, then insert several circles of blotting or filter paper to keep the rubber in place. Make sure the paper is a tight fit or the mosquito will almost certainly trap several legs in the gap. These will subsequently break off particularly if the specimens are left in the tube for any length of time. Caution—chloroform dissolves plastic.

The leaves of English, or hedge, laurel (from the Lower Mainland) can replace the chloroform-soaked rubber and will keep the mosquitoes relaxed for several days. Chop or crush the leaves and prepare the tube exactly as before. If the closed tube is subjected to extreme temperatures, water will condense on the walls and remove scales and hairs from the mosquito. The inside of the tube should be dried before use. If the leaves do not smell of almonds (cyanide) you have the wrong species of laurel.

Male and female mosquitoes can be swept from vegetation with a rugged insect net. Again moisture can ruin specimens, so sweeping may be unprofitable in the lower Mainland or interior wet belt. Males can be collected from swarms at sunrise and sunset. There is still some controversy over the function of this swarming behaviour and any females flying around or into the swarm should be noted and collected if possible.

Adults caught in nets can be emptied into a wide-mouthed (about 5 cm) killing jar, prepared in the same way as the tube. Alternatively, the adults can be sucked out of the net with an aspirator. My version, there are several, consists of a length of glass tubing 25 cm long and 1 cm diameter. One end is covered with a piece of insect screening held onto the glass by latex rubber tubing slipped over it (Fig. 3). Mosquitoes are simply sucked into the glass tube and held there until a killing tube is in place. Then they

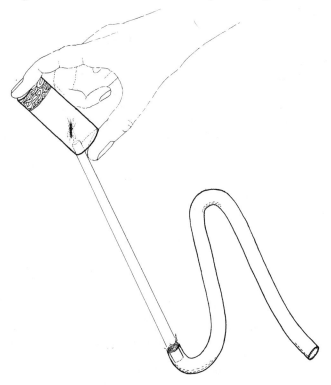

Fig. 3.   Killing tube and aspirator.

are blown gently back to the open end where they will walk upwards, or towards the the light, into the killing tube. Beware of condensation on the inside of the glass if the tube is cold. The tendency for adults to fly upwards can be used to keep mosquitoes in inverted nets. You may end up with your head and aspirator inside the net if you cannot see through it from the outside. This, and similar behaviour, is guaranteed to amuse spectators and is good for public relations.

Mounting Adults

Adults should be mounted on pins as soon as possible after they are killed. The simplest way is to glue them directly onto a 0 or 1 insect pin (see Appendix, p. 178) using a small dot of shellac gel. The gel is picked up on another pin and a narrow ring transferred to the mounting pin, as the latter is rolled between finger and thumb. This ring of shellac should be applied a third of the way down the pin from its head. The mosquito should then be arranged on its left side and the sticky pin pressed gently onto the right side of the thorax, just anterior to the wing. Holding the pin vertically, the mosquito can be adjusted so that its body is horizontal and the legs and wing on the left side do not obscure setae and scales on the thorax. Don't forget to include a label before putting the specimen into a freezer to dry for about four to six weeks. Specimens (adults, larvae, or slides with parts) should always be labelled with date and place of capture and, once they have been identified, with the name of the species.

To prepare shellac gel, boil 50 ml (2 oz.) of white shellac for five minutes, then add a few drops of polyvinyl alcohol (PVA) solution and continue boiling for two or three more minutes. Cool rapidly by pouring into screw-top or snap-cap vials standing in cold water. The gel should be the consistency of petroleum jelly; the PVA prevents the gel from separating out during storage. White shellac is flammable and should be boiled in a heatproof glass or metal container in a pan of water.

Larvae

Mosquito larvae can be found in almost any still or slowly flowing water that persists for four or more weeks.

Professional mosquito surveyors scoop up larvae using a dipper which is a white cup, with a capacity of about 500 ml, on the end of a long handle. A white plastic container (like those used for dairy products) makes a reasonable substitute. These usually have watertight lids and can be used to carry larvae for short distances.

The technique when dipping in open water is to wait motionless until a good portion of the larvae are at the surface and then slide the cup quickly under them. If the site is deep and clear, a plankton net or a strainer can be used to concentrate the larvae. For small pools a bulb pipette can be used. The best is a protozoa, or basting, pipette with a glass barrel, but a pipette can be improvised from glass or plastic tubing with a suitable large rubber bulb. If the pool is on a slope or if a cavity of a rotting tree is to be investigated, a length of flexible plastic tubing, about 1 cm in diameter, can be used to siphon liquid and larvae.

A photographic developing tray, or a white enamel dish, can be used to sort the larvae from other insects and debris. Large samples can be concentrated by pouring them into a jar lined with a tightly fitting, open cylinder, of insect screen which can be raised to project several centimetres above the rim so that the water flows out and the larvae remain in the jar.

Anopheline larvae often float among the vegetation at the edge of a pool or ditch where it is difficult to sweep. These can be collected by pressing a container or dipper slowly into the water until the surface almost reaches the rim and then allowing the water to rush in from the direction of the larvae.

When larvae are being brought back from a collecting trip they should be kept cool and not shaken violently. Because they can survive for several hours without access to the surface, larvae can be transported, with less damage, if the container is filled to the brim. For longer journeys, strong plastic bags, three-quarters full and twisted and tied at the top, work well for both larvae and pupae. Some collectors hang these from a rack in their vehicle. For valuable specimens, or in very hot weather, a picnic cooler with ice or cold packs can be used to hold the plastic bags.

Mounting Larvae

To make a reference collection of larvae, some specimens of each species encountered should be reared to the fourth instar and then identified as described on pages 40 to 45. If the identity of the larvae is uncertain some should be reared to adults and the remainder preserved in the following way. Pick up the larvae in a clean pipette and transfer them with a minimal amount of water to a small jar or tube containing a fixing fluid. One of the best is KAA fluid: Mix 1 part kerosene with 3 parts acetic acid and 30 parts ethyl or isopropyl alcohol. The larvae swell in this fluid and after an hour or so can be transferred to 70-95% alcohol. Ideal tubes for storing larvae can be obtained from any friendly dentist. These are the tubes used for local anaesthetic with a rubber plunger at one end and a membrane at the other. Removal of the plunger, however, is almost impossible without a hypodermic syringe. With a syringe, the plunger can easily be forced out of the tube by injecting alcohol through the membrane. The larva is then pipetted in and the plunger re-inserted. Air bubbles must be excluded and the tube carefully labelled if it is to be a long-lasting record. The most permanent label is a small piece of paper enclosed in the tube with the data written in India ink. Acid from the KAA in the specimen will fix the ink.

Larvae can be kept in any other small glass tubes but unless very tight neoprene stoppers are used there is a risk of the alcohol evaporating. Many museums store the vials on a pad of cotton wool in larger screw-topped jars also filled with alcohol. It is not safe to leave the tubes or vials out of sight for long. They should be examined and topped up if necessary every six months or so.

Most larvae can be identified using a good hand lens or a dissecting microscope but to see fine details or to keep a convenient reference collection, larvae or their cast skins can be mounted on microscope slides. Professional collectors may wish to make permanent slides using Canada balsam, but this is a time-consuming process and I usually mount larvae, skins or other mosquito parts (e.g. egg, pupal skin, adult palp, claw or genitalia) on slides with polyvinyl lactophenol, PVL. PVL mounts can be made in a few minutes because specimens do not have to be cleared in potassium hydroxide and dehydrated in alcohol, but are simply covered with a few drops of PVL on a slide, heated gently and then a glass cover slip placed on top. Although these slides are considered temporary, I have some that are unchanged after 15 years. Wood *et al*. (1979) give details of how to make permanent slides and Martin (1977) describes how to make and use PVL and other water-miscible media.

Pupae

Papae are collected and handled in the same way as larvae. Because living pupae are difficult to identify, the adults should be allowed to emerge. To preserve the pupal skins cut them open and mount flat in PVL on a slide, not forgetting the label.

Eggs

Most aedine mosquitoes pass the winter in the egg stage. The eggs of some species will hatch if immersed in water at any time of year. Others appear to require low, followed by high, temperature or changing day length or all of these before they will hatch.

Eggs can be separated from turf, mud or silt by flotation in a saturated solution of common salt, magnesium sulphate, or sugar (Service 1976), but because they can only be identified with certainty using a scanning electron microscope, it is more practical to attempt to hatch them. If a few are to be kept for measurement or study with a compound microscope they can be mounted as above.

IDENTIFICATION

As mentioned earlier, some mosquitoes must be reared from the larval stage if they are to be identified with certainty. Because several species often share the same breeding site, a number of species of larvae can be found in the same pool. A sample of the larvae should be reared to the last instar and sorted into species before they start to pupate. To do this, the beginner may have to kill representative specimens to look at the characters used in the keys. Once familiar with these characters, it should be possible to separate the remaining living larvae into their various species. If there is any doubt, or if you think there is a rare species present, larvae can be reared individually and their skins kept at each moult.

Pupae should be kept in cages or wide-mouthed jars in small shallow dishes of clean water with a piece of insect screen or clean twigs at the water surface onto which the newly emerged adults can climb. After 24 or more hours the adults can be killed and mounted. Even if the larvae are lost, reared specimens are more certainly indentified than wild ones in which the scales are often rubbed off.

According to the latest *Catalog of Mosquitoes* (Knight & Stone 1977), which is accepted by most North American experts, the Family Culicidae has three Subfamilies, only two of which have representatives in British Columbia—the Anophelinae and Culicinae. Each Subfamily is further divided into tribes which are represented in the Province by one genus each. These divisions are shown in Table III.

Arrangement of Taxa

Names and their order are based on Knight & Stone 1977

Family Dixidae

Family Chaoboridae

Family Culicidae

    Subfamily Anophelinae

        Tribe Anophelini

        Genus *Anopheles*

    Subfamily Culicinae

        Tribe Aedini

            Genus *Aedes*

        Tribe Culicini

            Genus *Culex*

        Tribe Culisetini

            Genus *Culiseta*

        Tribe Mansoniini

            Genus *Coquillettidia* (= *Mansonia*, see p. 169)

TABLE III

Keys are provided to assign adults and larvae to a genus. Following these are keys to species of the four main genera (the fifth having only one species). With a little experience some specimens can be assigned to a genus by eye. If this is done, the keys to species can be entered directly.

Male mosquitoes do not bite and are encountered less often than females. For this reason I have not included separate keys for males. In some cases males can be identified to species using the keys to females. Characters such as the colour and distribution of the scales on the thorax, abdomen, wings and legs are similar in both sexes, although the scales of the male seem to rub off more easily than those of the female. The hind tarsal claws are usually similar to the fore claws of the corresponding females; these are illustrated when they are used to separate similar species. References to tarsal claws in the text are to the fore claws of the female. Males can be identified to species with accuracy if the last few abdominal segments are cut off, made transparent, and examined under a dissecting microscope. When differences in these genitalia can be used to separate species with similar females or larvae they are mentioned in the descriptions. Illustrations of the male genitalia and keys to males of species found in British Columbia can be found in Carpenter & La Casse (1955) and Wood *et al.* (1979).

Using the keys

, Keys are made up of couplets. At each couplet the user must decide on one of two descriptions. When the key ends at a genus or species the complete description should be examined, particularly if there is doubt about the identification. If the description, including habitat, does not fit the specimen, it is possible to work backwards through the key to the previous couplet (the number in parenthesis). Some of the species will "key out" in more than one place if a character is present in some specimens but not in others. This is noted by (in part) below the specific name.

To keep the keys concise, several technical terms are used. These are illustrated in the figures and defined in the glossary. Some of the terms are discussed below.

Colour is occasionally used in the keys. At, best, colour is subjective and, unfortunately, that of the scales of the adult fades with time, particularly if specimens are left in the light. When colours are mentioned in the description, they refer to specimens less than one year old.

Most measurements used in the keys are comparative. If length or width is not indicated on the accompanying diagram, it is taken at the longest or widest part.

When the term *basal* is used to describe a character (e.g., tarsal band) it refers to the area closest to the centre of the body; the terms *distal* or *apical* refer to areas furthest away from the centre or closest to the apex. *Median* describes an area close to the mid-line; *lateral* further away.

Some of the characters can be seen with a 20x hand lens, others require the use of a 50x dissecting microscope, but the serrations on the pecten teeth and fine spines on the comb scales, shown enlarged in the larval diagrams, require a compound microscope with about 200x magnification. Magnifications in parenthesis are included in the keys where needed.

Larvae

The term seta (plural setae) is now used instead of the "hairs," "tufts" or "bristles" of early authors, and is restricted to a cuticular outgrowth with a socket at its base. Most of the setae are in fact sense organs with nerves running from them to the central nervous system. Even if they are broken off it is possible to see their position because the sockets are visible with a compound microscope.

To understand the characters used in the keys and in the diagrams accompanying the species descriptions, it will help to look at a labelled diagram of a generalized mosquito larva. Figure 4 comprises a dorsal view of the head and thorax; Figure 5 is a lateral view of a typical abdominal segment (A-II); and Figure 6, a lateral view of the terminal abdominal segments (A-VIII, A-X and Siphon). Most of the setae are shown but only those used in the keys and species descriptions are labelled. Although I refer to the setae singly in the keys and descriptions they are almost always in symmetrical pairs on either side of the body. In the diagrams, however, I have shown them only on one side.

On the antenna, seta 1-A, often called the antennal "tuft," is unbranched in some species, branched in others. The cranial setae on the dorsal surface of the head are numbered 1 to 7-C. Only some are used in my keys. 2 and 3-C, the inner and outer clypeal seta, respectively, are long and prominent only in the anophelines (Fig. 16, p. 57). Setae 5, 6 and 7-C are long in the aedines. They usually arise in a prominent triangular group with 5-C closer to the rear of the head than 6-C (normal position). In most early works 5-C and 6-C were referred to as "upper" and "lower head hairs" respectively. Seta 7-C is the preantennal "tuft" close to the base of the antenna. In the anophenlines and a few aedines, 5, 6 and 7-C arise more or less side by side forming a conspicuous row.

The three thoracic segments are fused and enlarged in mosquitoes. Setae 1 to 3-P of the prothorax, used in the keys, are illustrated on the left side of the generalized larva and on the diagrams accompanying the species descriptions. Mesothoracic setae 1 to 4-M are shown on the right side of the thorax, so that their size and branching can be compared from species to species.

41

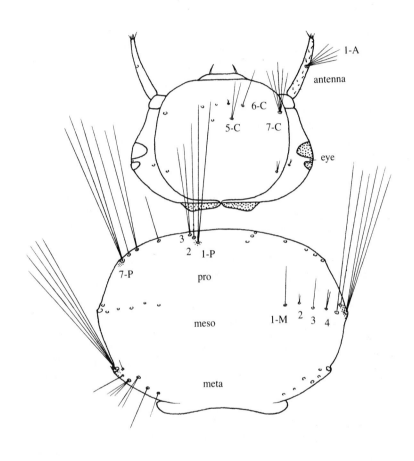

Fig. 4.   Head and thorax generalized mosquito larva (dorsal view): 1-A = antennal seta; 5-C to 7-C = cranial setae; 1-P to 3-P and 7-P = prothoracic setae; pro = prothorax; 1-M to 4-M = mesothoracic setae; meso = mesothorax; meta = metathorax.

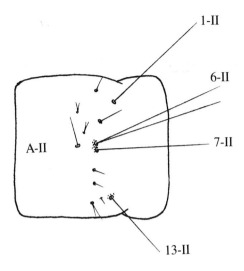

Fig. 5. Second abdominal segment (A-II), generalized mosquito (lateral view): 1-II = dorsolateral; 6-II = lateral; 7-II = sublateral; 13-II = ventrolateral abdominal setae.

The abdominal segments are given Roman numerals, A-I to A-X. On a typical segment (A-II) the longest setae are: dorsolaterals, 1-AII; laterals, 6-AII; sublaterals, 7-AII; and ventrolaterals, 13-AII. In the anophenlines, the dorsolateral setae are palmate and hydrophobic, sometimes called "float hairs" (Fig. 17, p. 58). The so-called "lateral hairs" of the most early papers usually refer to lateral seta 6 but perhaps sometimes also to sublateral seta 7. The number of branches of these setae have been and still are used in many keys. I have avoided using them because of the possible confusion of 6 with 7 and the variability in the number of their branches.

The three apical abdominal segments are unlike the preceeding ones. On segment A-VIII there are five large setae, the "pentad hairs" of early workers, and the comb scales which are flattened spines rigidly attached to the cuticle. The number, arrangement and shape (200x) of the scales are used in most keys. Segment A-IX is the sclerotised respiratory tube, called the siphon, S. Some authors consider it to be part of VIII as well as

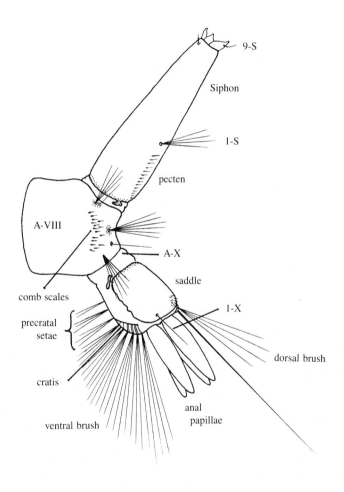

Fig. 6. Terminal abdominal segments (A-VIII, A-X, and Siphon), generalized mosquito (lateral view): A-VIII = eighth abdominal segment; A-X = anal segment; 1-S and 9-S = siphon setae; 1-X = saddle seta.

IX. The siphonal index is a ratio of its length: width (i.e., 3x1 means that it is three times as long as broad). The pecten is a row of thorn-like spines on either side of the siphon. Their arrangement and the number of cusps at the base of each pecten tooth (200x) is used in many keys. The pecten is called uneven when one or more of the distal teeth is "detached," i.e., spaced more widely apart than the rest. The large ventral seta on the siphon, 1-S, is many-branched in most fourth instar larvae and has been called the siphon "tuft." It may be inserted at the base of the siphon or within or beyond the pecten. Seta 9-S, located on the ventrolateral flaps at the apex of the siphon is hooked in some species with long siphons and may be used to anchor the larva. The anal segment, A-X, has a dorsal sclerotised area, the saddle, which completely surrounds the segment in a few species. 1-X is the largest lateral seta, usually called the "saddle hair" in early papers because in most aedines it is inserted on the saddle. Segment X also carries the dorsal and ventral "brushes." These are the main swimming setae and are long and plentiful in most aedines but rather sparse on larvae inhabiting rot cavities in trees, presumably because these larvae travel less. The distal setae of the ventral "brush" are attached to a sclerotised grid, the cratis. Hence the name precratal "tufts" for the one or more branched setae which, in some species arise anterior to the cratis on the ventral side of X. In the diagrams accompanying each species, the cratis is drawn but the dorsal and ventral setae have been omitted or shortened for clarity. The anal papillae, often called "gills" are not respiratory but are osmotic and ionic regulators. Their shape and length compared with the saddle is sometimes used in the keys but their length may vary inversely with the salinity of the breeding site. The aci (singular acus) are small anterior projections of the saddle and siphonal sclerites.

Adults

Adults should be mounted on the right side so that the left aspect is exposed. They can then be compared with Fig. 7 which shows the left side of the head and thorax of a generalized female mosquito.

The colour of the scales and the underlying cuticle can best be seen with a hand lens in diffuse light. With a dissecting microscope, the shape and curvature of the scales will be obvious, but I find that the specimen must be rotated under the microscope and viewed against a matte gray

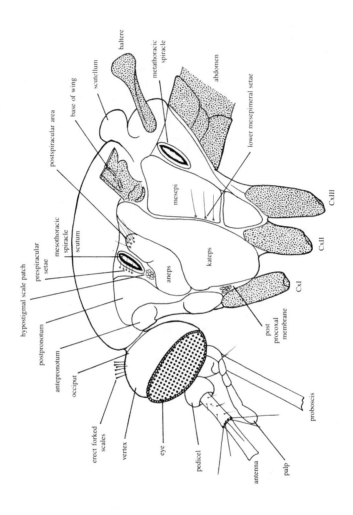

Fig. 7. Head and thorax, generalized female mosquito (lateral view):aneps = anepisternum; Cx I, Cx II, Cx III = fore, mid and hind coxae; kateps = katepisternum; mesepi = mesepimeron.

background otherwise some of the iridescent and shiny dark scales may appear to be pale. Pointing the bases of the scales towards the microscope lamp reduces the reflections.

The dorsal surface of the head is covered with scales and these tend to stay attached even when those on the scutum are rubbed off. I have used the colour of the erect forked scales on the rear (occiput) and top (vertex) of the head to separate some species. These can be seen with a hand lens but warnings about reflections and fading must be kept in mind. Much of the surface of the head is taken up by the compound eyes. The long slender, scaly proboscis projects forward, flanked by the antennae and the palps. The enlarged segment at the base of the antenna is the pedicel. The palps have five segments in the male and appear to have two to four in the females.

As in the larva, the thorax consists of three fused segments, the pro, meso and metathorax. Their sclerotised cuticle is called notum dorsally, sternum ventrally and pleuron laterally. The pronotum (dorsal surface of the prothorax) is displaced laterally and divided into antepronotum and postpronotum. The latter bears setae on some species. Between the fore coxae (basal segment of the front legs) lies the probasisternum. It can be seen best from the front of the specimen (Fig. 8) and bears setae and scales in some species. Behind the fore coxae lies the postprocoxal membrane. In some species there is a patch of scales, the postprocoxal scale patch, on this membrane. The largest dorsal region of the thorax is the scutum (part of the mesonotum). Behind it lie the narrower scutellum and postnotum. The differently coloured scales of the scutum, contrasting with each other and the underlying cuticle, produce patterns which are useful in separating some species. Figure 9 shows the terms used to describe these patterns. The depression at the rear of the scutum, between the wings, is the prescutellar space. The mesopleuron (Fig. 7) is divided obliquely into a large anterior region, the mesepisternum and a smaller posterior mesepimeron. The mesepisternum is divided transversely into dorsal anepisternum and ventral katepisternum. The latter is easily recognized even in very scaly species by its ham-like shape. Following Wood *et al.* (1979) three areas of the anepisternum are defined each bearing taxonomically important scales or setae. Immediately below the mesothoracic spiracle lies the hypostigmal area, below that lies the subspiracular area and immediately behind the spiracle, the postspiracular area. Close to the front of the mesothoracic spiracle a row of fine

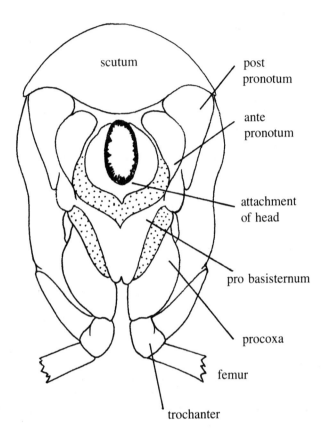

Fig. 8. Thorax, generalized female mosquito (viewed from front, head removed).

prespiracular setae is present in some genera. The position of scales and setae on the katepisternum varies in the aedines. The mesepimeron bears both upper and lower mesepimeral setae in some species. The numbers of lower mesepimeral setae differ from species to species and when present are arranged in a vertical row on the anterior of the ventral half of the sclerite.

The wings are long and slender. The veins are usually covered with scales whose colour and pattern is used in the keys. The names of the veins mentioned in the descriptions are shown in Figure 10.

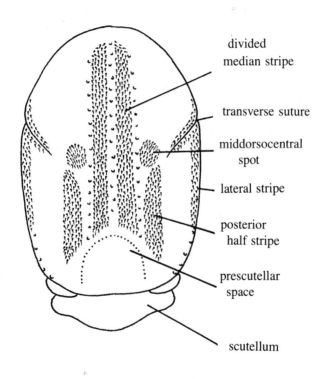

divided
median stripe

transverse suture

middorsocentral
spot

lateral stripe

posterior
half stripe

prescutellar
space

scutellum

Fig. 9.   Thorax, generalized female mosquito (dorsal view).

There are three pairs of legs, fore, mid and hind. Each has a basal coxa, a smaller trochanter followed by the two largest segments, the femur and tibia and ending in the tarsus (Fig. 11). The so-called "knee spot" refers to a patch of pale scales at the apical end of the femur. The tarsi have five segments (tarsomeres) and bear a pair of curved claws at the apex. The presence or absence of bands of scales on the tarsomeres separate the "striped-leg" and "black-leg" mosquitoes of early workers.

The female abdomen has eight visible segments. The dorsal sclerotised surface of each segment is a tergite, ventrally a sternite. Segments IX and X are collapsed within segment VIII and a pair of long cerci projects in most aedines giving the tip of the abdomen a pointed appearance (Table I, p. 17). In the male, segments IX and X rotate through 180° allowing males to clasp females "face to face" while mating. Pivoting on tergite IX (and therefore ventral) is a pair of claspers made up of a basal gonocoxite and a distal gonostyle. In aedines the gonocoxites are conspicuous but in other genera they are apposed and less obvious (Fig. 13, p. 52).

Guide to Treatment of Species

Descriptions of species are headed with the currently used scientific name, followed by the name used in the original description. Below these are synonyms that have been used, sometimes incorrectly, in papers dealing with British Columbian mosquitoes and, finally, a translation of the scientific name.

The first paragraph of the description gives the overall appearance of the adult. The presence or absence of bands on the tarsi is an important taxonomic character and can usually be seen with the naked eye on both males and females (you will, however, need a lens to see if the bands are at the base or apex of the segments). Size is variable, depending on rearing conditions, and is given as a guide. If, however, two species are collected at the same time, or are reared under the same conditions, their relative sizes should be correct, i.e., a large species will be larger than a medium sized one. Criteria used are—small, wing length 3.5–4.0 mm; medium, 4.0–4.5; large, 4.5–6.0.

The second paragraph describes the adult females in more detail.

Descriptions of the larvae are terse as an accompanying diagram shows the main characters of each species.

This is followed by notes on the life history, habits and distribution of the species. Its habitat and biotic zone can often be useful in making an identification, but note that mosquitoes have been collected systematically in only a few regions of the Province.

Finally, if the species is a pest in British Columbia, some control measures are suggested.

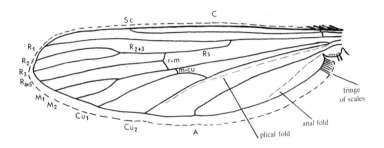

Fig. 10. Wing, generalized mosquito: A = anal vein; C = costa; Cu = cubitus; M = media; R = radius; Sc = subcosta; r-m, m-cu = crossveins.

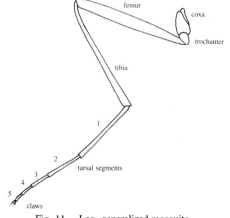

Fig. 11. Leg, generalized mosquito.

Keys to Genera

Adults in British Columbia

1.   Scutellum crescent-shaped, setae on margin evenly distributed (Fig. 12a); palps of female about as long as proboscis .... *Anopheles* (p. 56)

        Scutellum trilobed with setae in tufts on lobes (Fig. 12b); palps of female much shorter than proboscis 2

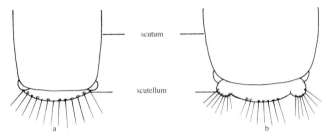

Fig. 12.   Scutum and scutellum: a, anopheline; b, aedine.

2.   (1) Postspiracular setae present; cerci showing, apex of female abdomen pointed; gonocoxites of male long, separated and projecting (Fig. 13a) .... *Aedes* (p. 63)

        Postspiracular setae absent; female abdomen bluntly rounded; male gonocoxites short and folded together (Fig. 13b) 3

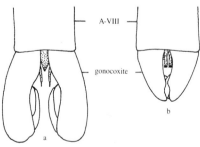

Fig. 13.   Eighth abdominal segment (A-VIII) and gonocoxites; a, *Aedes;* b, *Culex.*

3. (2) Prespiracular setae present; crossveins r-m and m-cu
close together (Fig. 14a)............................*Culiseta* (p. 156)
Prespiracular setae absent; crossveins separated by more
than length of crossvein m-cu (Fig. 14b)...........................4

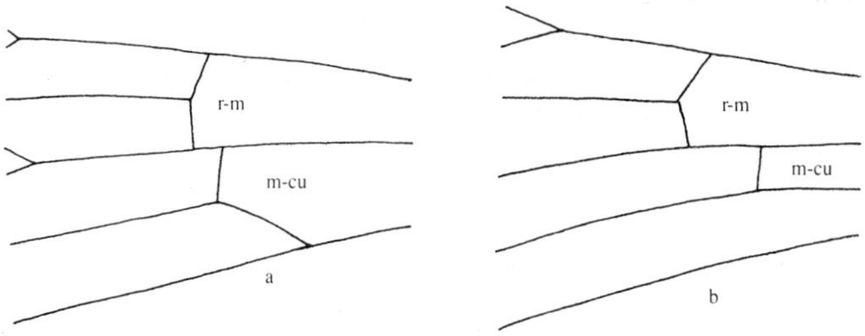

Fig. 14.   Wing venation: a, *Culiseta;* b, *Culex.*

4. (3) Wing scales narrow, dark; first tarsal segments without a
pale band at midlength.....................................*Culex* (p. 146)
Wing scales broad, dark and pale mixed; first tarsal segments with a pale band at midlength *Mansonia* (p. 169)

Fourth instar larvae in British Columbia

1.   Head and body slender, larva lying horizontally when at
surface; no posterior tubular siphon......*Anopheles* (p. 56)
Head broad; larvae usually hang vertically from surface
by long posterior siphon...2
2. (1) Associated with plant roots; siphon serrated at apex; no
pecten...*Mansonia* (p. 169)
Free swimming; siphon tubular at apex; pecten present........ 3
3. (2) Siphon with one pair of branched setae near its base, not
on apical ⅔...*Culiseta* (p. 157)
One or more pairs of branched setae on apical ⅔ of
siphon..4
4. (3) Siphon with one pair of ventral branched setae (additional dorsal setae found in *Ae. provocans*)
....*Aedes* (p. 71)
Siphon with 4 or more pairs of ventral branched setae
....*Culex* (p. 148)

53

Genus *Anopheles*

Anopheles Meigen, 1818, Syst.Beschr.Zweifl.Ins. 1:10

Anopheles is the Greek word for troublesome.

Anopheline mosquitoes are different in many respects from other genera. Because of these differences they were placed in a separate tribe Anophelini (Carpenter & La Casse 1955) and more recently in a separate subfamily Anophelinae (Knight & Stone 1977).

All stages of anophelines are distinct from other mosquitoes in British Columbia and there should be no difficulty in identifying them in the field. Adults have narrow wings and look very long and slender. They often adopt the well-known resting attitude, illustrated in Table I (p. 17), where the mosquito almost stands on its head with the proboscis, thorax and abdomen in a straight line. They indubitably adopted this position long before the evolution of man, but one is tempted to think of it as cryptic adaptation when they sit on rough-cut wooden surfaces looking deceptively like splinters.

The palps of both males and females are about as long as the proboscis; those of the male look bushy because of the long apical setae. All our species have the dark scales on some of the wing veins aggregated into spots or patches. In both sexes, the posterior margin of the scutellum is evenly rounded with a fringe of regularly distributed setae and the abdomen bears setae but no scales.

The females hibernate and can be found in winter resting under culverts, bridges and eaves and inside sheds where they usually settle in the roof. Far from civilization they hibernate in burrows, caves, hollow trees and other sheltered places.

The eggs are laid singly among vegetation at the margin of bodies of fresh water—from lakes to small ditches with slowly-flowing water. The eggs have buoyant lateral ''wings,'' not found in our other mosquitoes, and they float horizontally.

The larvae are slim, their head and thorax relatively narrower than in the other genera. Special fan-shaped (palmate) setae on the dorsal surface of the abdomen enable them to float horizontally. In this position the eighth segment can break through the surface film. They feed here on particles from the film or ''graze'' on larger particles below the surface and on the bottom. Anopheline larvae have an extremely short respiratory siphon. The pecten, unlike that of our other mosquitoes does not

54

have separate teeth, but is part of a sclerotised plate on segment VIII. Because there are few differences between the larvae of the three anophelines found in the Province, only *An. earlei* is illustrated (Fig. 18, p. 59).

Larvae from the related families Chaoboridae and Dixidae can be misidentified as anophelines. Chaoborid larvae, however, have prehensile antennae and are all predaceous. Of the species that could be confused with mosquito larvae, the commonest in this area is *Eucorethra underwoodi* which has no siphon and floats horizontally on the surface. It has a squarish head and stout bristly looking thorax and should not be difficult to identify when once seen with the slimmer anophelines. If any chaoborid larvae are reared or collected they should be separated from the mosquitoes or there may be a sharp decline in the population of the latter. Although the dixids are dark and slim like anophelines, they have the unusual habit of attaching themselves to the sides of a container in the shape of a U.

Anopheline pupae are not markedly different from those of other genera. A key that separates pupae to their genera is found in Bohart and Washino (1978).

Genus *Anopheles*

Key to adult females in British Columbia

1.   Wing veins with several irregular patches of pale scales (Fig. 15a). Lower Mainland and southern Vancouver Island.................................*punctipennis* (p. 61)
    Wing veins entirely dark-scaled..............................2

2. (1) Scales fringing wing tip all dark (Fig. 15b). Dry interior of Province.................................*freeborni* (p. 60)
    Some scales fringing wing tip pale—silver, yellow or bronzy (Fig. 15c). Widespread distribution *earlei* (p. 58)

Key to fourth instar larvae in British Columbia

1.   Inner clypeal setae 2-C forked at apex (Fig. 16a), one or rarely both setae may be unforked in the odd specimen.................................*earlei* (p. 58)
    Setae 2-C not forked at apex (Fig. 16b)..............................2

2. (1) Seta 1-A inserted in apical ¾ of antenna; abdominal segments IV–VII with median and small paired lateral sclerites (Fig. 17). Dry interior.........*freeborni* (p. 60)
    1-A in basal ¼ of antenna; segments AIV–AVII with a median pigmented sclerite. Lower Mainland and southern Vancouver Island.................*punctipennis* (p. 61)

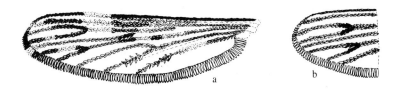

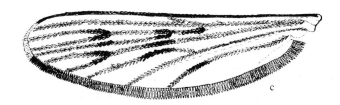

Fig. 15.   Wing: a, *An. punctipennis;* b, *An. freeborni;* c, *An. earlei.*

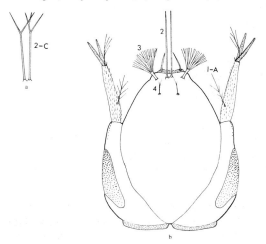

Fig. 16.   a. Inner clypeal setae: 2-C = *An. earlei.*b. Head, *An. freeborni:* 1-A = antennal seta; 2, 3 and 4 = inner, outer and post clypeal setae.

57

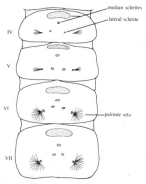

Fig. 17. Abdominal segments IV–VII, *An. freeborni*.

Anopheles earlei Vargas

Anopheles earlei Vargas, 1943, Bol.Of.Sanit.Pan-Amer. 22:8
Anopheles maculipennis: of authors, not Meigen
Anopheles occidentalis: of authors, not Dyar & Knab
(named after W. C. Earle, a malariologist who worked in the West Indies)

Figs. 15c, wing; 16a, inner clypeal setae

A large species; wing-length 5–6 mm. The wings have dark spots and a diagnostic patch of pale fringe scales (silver, yellow or bronze) at the tip.

Female—Proboscis and palps dark brown. Scutum with scattered yellow setae and a broad grey median stripe with a waxy bloom. Legs black with a bluish iridescence and a few scattered yellow scales at the apices of tibiae and femora. Wings with narrow, dark brown scales usually clustered to form 4 darker spots; wing tips with a patch of light fringe scales (Fig. 15c).

Larva Fig. 18—Inner clypeal seta, 2-C, forked distally into 2 to 5 branches; outer clypeal, 3-C,5 or more branched distally; post clypeal, 4-C,0 to 5-branched, 4 or 5 in most specimens. The abdominal segments have 2 dark median sclerites, the anterior one about as wide as the distance between the palmate setae. These are found in all 3 anophelines.

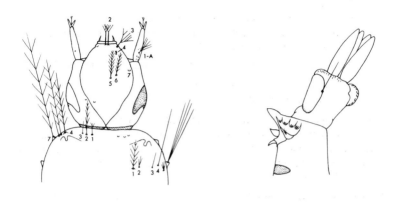

Fig. 18.   Larva, *An. earlei.*

In the past this species was confused with *occidentalis* which is similar but which is now thought to extend only as far north as Oregon (Curtis's remarks about *occidentalis* in 1967 are now believed to refer to *earlei*), and it was misnamed *maculipennis* (by Hearle, Gibson and others), a species not found in Canada.

An. earlei is widely distributed in British Columbia but less common in the lower Fraser Valley than *punctipennis.* The larvae develop in very cold water, usually in a slowly flowing stream or ditch with emergent marginal vegetation and in irrigation seepage in the interior. The females bite viciously and will enter houses in search of blood meals. They can attack in air so cold that no other mosquitoes are flying and are the only anophelines found in the Yukon or Alaska. In a paper entitled *Canada's National Mosquito?* Hudson (1978) reports finding large numbers of *earlei* females, many of which were engorged with blood, in a beaver lodge in central Alberta. This is obviously an ideal place for a mosquito to spend the winter. It is a host of western equine encephalitis (WEE) in Saskatchewan (Hayles *et al.* 1979).

Anopheles freeborni Aitken

Anopheles maculipennis freeborni Aitken, 1939, Pan.Pac.Ent. 15:192

Anopheles quadrimaculatus: of authors, not Say

(named after S. B. Freeborn who pioneered research on malaria in California in the early 1900's)

Figs. 15b, wing tip; 16b, head; 17, abdominal segments IV–VII

A medium to large species; wing length 4.5–5.5 mm. Scales on surface and fringe of wing uniformly dark brown.

Female—Scutum with a median grey stripe and narrow yellow scales. Scutellum with short golden brown and long dark setae. Legs black; apices of tibiae and femora with pale yellow scales. It is very similar to *earlei* apart from the wings which lack the patch of pale fringe scales near the tip (Fig. 15b).

Larva—Seta 1-A inserted more distally on antenna than that of *punctipennis*. Clypeal setae, 2-C, unbranched and close together, 3-C many-branched and fan-shaped, 4-C 2 to 5-branched (Fig. 16b). In addition to the median sclerites found on the abdominal segments of all 3 anophelines, *freeborni* has a pair of small lateral sclerites (Fig. 17). These are not present on any of the *punctipennis* larvae I have examined from the Lower Mainland.

This species, which was called *quadrimaculatus* until 1939, breeds mainly in clear water in open sunny situations, such as irrigation seepage. Phytoplankton at the surface may be a source of food as the gut of the larva is often green. It can tolerate some pollution but is not found in brackish water. Adults frequently enter houses to hibernate. Hadwen (1915) first discovered it in the Province at Keremeos when he heard about unconfirmed cases of malaria in the neighbourhood.

It is found in the Okanagan and the Kootenays. Curtis's (1967a) report of its occurrence in the Fraser Valley was probably from the dry upper valley, north of Lytton, because it has not been found in the lower Fraser Valley. It occurs nowhere else in Canada but can be found in the Great Basin and the central valleys of California, Washington and Oregon (Bohart & Washino 1978). It is potentially an effective vector of malaria and has been found naturally infected with WEE virus but is not sufficiently numerous to be important in this connection.

Anopheles punctipennis (Say)

Culex punctipennis Say, 1823, J.Acad.Sci.Nat. Phila. 3:9
(Latin: wings marked with punctures, referring to their many small patches of yellowish scales)

Fig. 15a, wing

A medium to large species; wing length 5–5.5 mm. Wings with dark aggregates of scales and with several smaller patches of pale yellow scales.

Female—Proboscis dark, palps with raised scales on basal portion. Scutum has a broad median stripe with a waxy bloom, bearing narrow greyish scales. Abdomen dark grey with light and dark setae. Legs dark, pale-scaled at apices of femora and tibiae. Wings predominantly dark-scaled with scattered clusters of pale yellow scales.

Larva—Seta 1-A inserted more basally on antenna than in the very similar species, *freeborni*. Inner clypeal seta, 2-C, unbranched. There are no small lateral pigmented sclerites on the abdominal segments.

The only anopheline so far found on Vancouver Island, *punctipennis* is commoner than *earlei* in the lower Fraser Valley and has also been reported from the Kamloops area. As it has been found with *freeborni* in northern Idaho (Gjullin & Eddy 1972), it may also occur in the Kootenays although I was unable to find it there. The larvae breed in almost any type of water. Females bite freely after dark and are persistent in entering houses but are not numerous nor considered of importance as disease carriers.

This page (and pages 83, 97, 141, and 151) have been intentionally left blank to keep figures and relevant text together.

Genus *Aedes*

Aedes Meigen, 1818, Syst. Beschr. Zweifl. Ins. 1:13

Aëdes is the Greek word for disagreeable. Without the dieresis the word means house or building. Although Meigen did not use a dieresis, he translated it as troublesome. Some authorities, therefore, write the generic name *Aëdes*.

Most species of British Columbian mosquitoes belong to this genus. The females all have short palps, usually less than one quarter of the length of the proboscis, and in both sexes the posterior margin of the scutellum is tri-lobed with the setae in three tufts.

Aedes is a large and variable genus and in the field the most reliable character to separate females from other mosquito genera is the pointed abdomen. Males can be identified in the field by their large and separated gonocoxites but if these are not obvious the thorax can be examined for the presence of postspiracular setae which are absent in the males of *Culex, Culiseta,* and *Mansonia.* A slide of the terminalia, as well as confirming the genus, can be used to determine the species. (See Wood *et al.* 1979).

When at the water surface, the larvae of all culicines hang downwards from the hydrophobic tip of the siphon and are thus easily distinguished from anophelines.

Aedes larvae can be distinguished from those of *Culex* and *Culiseta* by the position of the siphon seta (1-S). It is never at the base of the siphon in aedines and can be seen with a hand lens if the larva cooperates.

The pupae are hard to identify. It is usually simpler to let them emerge.

Nearly all aedine adults in British Columbia die in late summer or autumn. The eggs are laid singly or in clusters, usually in crevices at the margins of suitable breeding sites. They do not float. Most aedines overwinter as eggs.

Genus *Aedes*

Key to adult females in British Columbia

---

* Not yet found in British Columbia.

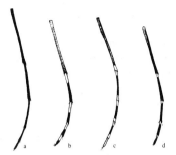

Fig. 19.   Hind tarsi: a, *Ae. diantaeus*; b, *Ae. excrucians*; c, *Ae. dorsalis*; d, *Ae. vexans*.

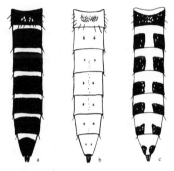

Fig. 20.   Abdominal tergites: a. *Ae. aboriginis*; b. *Ae. flavescens*; c. *Ae. nigromaculis*.

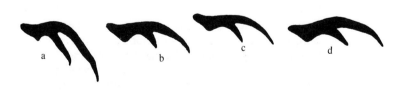

Fig. 21.   Tarsal claws: a. *Ae. excrucians*; b. *Ae. aloponotum*; c. *Ae. fitchii*; d. *Ae. euedes*.

65

8. (7) Abdominal tergites black with crisp white basal bands; no hypostigmal scale patch. Lower Fraser Valley .... *aloponotum* (p.78)

Tergites with scattered pale scales making margins of bands ragged; hypostigmal scale patch present in most specimens. Peace River—prairie habitat .... *riparius* (p. 132)

9. (7) Lower mesepimeral setae absent 10

Lower mesepimeral setae 1–5 11

10. (9) Convex surface of tarsal claw as in Fig. 21c; scutum with a dark brown median band and pale scales on lateral margins in most specimens .... *fitchii* (p. 102) (in part)

Convex surface of claw as in Fig. 21d; scutum with reddish brown scales dorsally and laterally *euedes* (p. 98)

11. (9) Segments 3 & 4 of palps with complete white basal bands; abdominal sternite 1 with white scales in most specimens .... *increpitus* (p. 114)

Palps dark scaled or with a few pale scales at bases of segments 3 & 4; sternite AI bare 12

12. (11) Lower mesepimeral setae 3 or 4; wings dark scaled .... *mercurator* (p. 120)

Lower mesepimeral setae 1 or 2 in most specimens, seldom 3 or 4; wings with scattered pale scales .... *fitchii* (p.102) (in part)

13. (2) Wings with pale and dark scales intermixed or pale and dark on alternate veins 14

Wing scales all dark or with some white scales at bases of veins C, Sc or R 16

14. (13) Wing vein A dark scaled; a cluster of white scales at tip of palp; scales in 2 groups on posterior margin of katepisternum (Fig. 22a); tips of scales broadly rounded .... *melanimon* (p. 118)

Vein A pale scaled; a few white scales scattered along palps but not at tip; scales covering posterior margin of katepisternum (Fig. 22b), tips pointed 15

15. (14) Wing veins with pale and dark scales evenly mixed; tarsal claw as in Fig. 23a.................... *campestris* (p. 80)

Scales on vein R_{4+5} mostly dark; claw as in Fig. 23b .... *dorsalis* (p. 94)

16. (13) Apical segment of hind tarsus black; scutum with pattern of fine golden and brown lines. Coastal....... *togoi* (p. 142)

Apical tarsal segment white; scutal pattern of a few broad stripes. Woodland.. 17

17. (16) Wing with patch of white scales at base of C; hind tarsal segments 2 & 3 with apical bands much narrower than basal.................................... *sierrensis* (p. 134)

Wing with base of C dark; bands of segments 2 & 3 equally broad.. *canadensis* (p. 84)

18. (1) Vertex of head and lateral scutum with silvery white scales; abdominal tergites with incomplete basal bands .... *hendersoni* (p. 106)

Scales on vertex and lateral scutum dark or pale—not silvery; abdominal bands complete in some species, incomplete in others.. 19

19. (18) Wings with alternate light and dark scaled veins .... *spencerii* (p. 136)

Wing scales mainly dark; white scales, if any, only at base of C, Sc and R.. 20

20. (19) Postprocoxal scale patch absent.. 21

Postprocoxal scale patch present.. 26

21. (20) A circular patch of appressed shiny black scales behind each eye; lateral margins of abdominal tergites silvery scaled (Fig. 24a)...................................... *cinereus* (p. 88)

No dark patches behind eyes; tergites lacking silvery white lateral stripes.. 22

22. (21) Abdominal tergites with basal lateral triangular patches of pale scales, joined in some specimens by a narrow basal row of pale scales (Fig. 24b)......... *diantaeus* (p. 92)

Tergites with complete pale basal bands of at least 3 rows of scales.. 23

23. (22) Wing with base of C entirely pale scaled, pale section as long as palp.................................... *pullatus* (p. 128)

Base of C dark scaled or, at most, with a few white scales...... 24

67

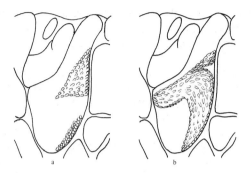

Fig. 22.   Katepisternum: a. *Ae. melanimon*; b. *Ae. dorsalis*.

Fig. 23.   Tarsal claws: a. *Ae. campestris* or *melanimon*; b. *Ae. dorsalis*.

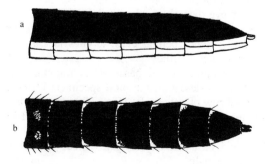

Fig. 24.   Abdominal tergites: a. *Ae. cinereus* (side view); b. *Ae. diantaeus*.

24. (23) Palps dark scaled; lower mesepimeral setae absent
.... *sticticus* (p. 138)
Palps dark, sprinkled with pale scales; lower mes-
epimeral setae 1 to 5 25

25. (24) Scales on mesepimeron extending to ventral margin;
dark brown median stripe on scutum contrasts with
yellow lateral areas in most specimens . . .
. . . *communis* (p. 90) and *nevadensis* (p. 122)
Mesepimeral scales extending no more than ¾ down
sclerite; scutum with uniformly light brown scales
.... *intrudens* (p. 116)

26. (20) Long black setae on anterior of post-pronotum and
scutum give thorax a hairy appearance 27
Setae on postpronotum restricted to a single row on
posterior margin; scutum with normal covering of
setae 28

27. (26) Tarsal claw abruptly curved beyond slender lateral tooth
(Fig. 25a) .... *impiger* (p. 110)
Claw gently curved, lateral tooth short and stout (Fig.
25b) .... *nigripes* (p. 122)

28. (26) Anepisternum extensively pale scaled around and below
spiracle; scattered pale scales at base of wing 29
Anepisternum bare around spiracle, or if some subspiracular scales present then wings with small
patches of pale scales at base—not scattered 30

29. (28) Erect forked scales of occiput dark; numerous pale scales
on C, Sc and in some specimens R .... *cataphylla* (p. 86)
Erect scales pale and dark mixed; wing veins dark with
compact basal patches of pale scales *provocans* (p. 126)

30. (28) Katepisternum with pale scales extending only ½ way
down sclerite, not reaching anterior angle at base of
anepisternum (Fig. 26a) .... *implicatus* (p. 112)
Pale scales extending about ⅔ down katepisternum,
reaching anterior angle at base of anepisternum (Fig.
26b) 31

Fig. 25.   Tarsal claws: a. *Ae. impiger*; b. *Ae. nigripes*.

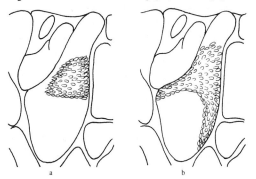

Fig. 26.   Katepisternum: a. *Ae. implicatus*; b. *Ae. pionips*.

31. (30) Setae of scutum and scutellum dark brown to black; fore
femora black with a distinct line of pale scales on
anterior surface .... *pionips* (p. 124)
Scutal and scutellar setae yellow to bronze; no distinct
line of pale scales on fore femora 32

32. (31) Palps and underside of proboscis speckled with yellowish
scales; abdominal tergite VII almost entirely pale
scaled .... *schizopinax**
Palps and proboscis dark; tergite AVII dark with a pale
basal band 33

---

* Not yet found in British Columbia.

33. (32) Probasisternum with scales and setae; a patch of pale
scales at base of vein C. Alpine .... *hexodontus* (p. 108)
Probasisternum bare; wing veins dark scaled or with very
few pale scales. Woodland 34
34. (33) Base of vein C invariably dark scaled; large species.
Coast forest .... *aboriginis* (p. 76)
Base of C with pale scales in some specimens; smaller
than, but hardly distinguishable from previous species. Widespread across province .... *punctor* (p. 130)

Genus *Aedes*

Key to fourth instar larvae in British Columbia

1. Saddle surrounding segment X 2
Saddle not surrounding X, or forming a narrow bridge
ventrally in some specimens 5
2. (1) Pecten with one or more apical teeth unevenly spaced on
siphon 3
Pecten teeth even or with a regular increase in spacing
towards apex 4
3. (2) Seta 1-S longer than diameter of tip of siphon, inserted
within pecten in basal ⅔ of siphon in most specimens
.... *nigripes* (p. 122)
1-S shorter than diameter of tip of siphon, inserted
beyond pecten in apical ⅓ .... *nigromaculis**
4. (2) Comb of 4 to 9 scales, typically 6; scales as long as apical
pecten tooth .... *hexodontus* (p. 108)
Comb of 9 to 20 scales; scales shorter than apical pecten
tooth .... *punctor* (p. 130)
5. (1) Saddle seta 1-X 2 or more branched 6
1-X unbranched 10
6. (5) Anal papillae large and leaflike; larvae in treeholes,
occasionally in artificial containers in woodland 7
Papillae tapering; larvae in groundwater (woodland,
open or floodwater) 8

---

* Not yet found in British Columbia.

71

7. (6) Pecten on basal ⅓ of siphon; more than 12 comb scales. Wherever there are deciduous trees .... *sierrensis* (p. 134)
Pecten covering more than basal ⅓ of siphon; less than 12 comb scales. Dry interior zones *hendersoni* (p. 106)

8. (6) More than 20 comb scales, typically about 35; pecten teeth evenly spaced. Open mountain pools .... *schizopinax**
Less than 20 comb scales; apical pecten teeth widely spaced 9

9. (8) Head setae 5 & 6-C more than 4-branched, in line with 7-C. Open or woodland pools .... *cinereus* (p. 88)
Setae 5 & 6-C usually 4 & 2-branched respectively, a line drawn through 5 & 6 intersects margin of head anterior to 7-C. Floodwater.................................. *vexans* (p. 144) (in part)

10. (5) Antennae longer than head, straight............... *diantaeus* (p. 92)
Antennae shorter than head, curved.. 11

11. (10) Siphon short and broad, less than 4×1, tapering slightly—tip more than ½ maximum width...................... 18
Siphon long, more than 4×1, tapering to less than ½ maximum width at tip.. 12

12. (11) 19 or fewer comb scales.................................. 13
20 or more comb scales................................ 15

13. (12) Pecten teeth evenly spaced.....................................*fitchii* (p. 102)
1 or more teeth widely spaced.. 14

14. (13) 6 to 9 comb scales; 1-S inserted in basal ⅔ of siphon. Northern grassland—Peace River............. *riparius* (p. 132)
11 to 19 comb scales; 1-S in apical ⅓ of siphon. Grassland—widespread.................................... *euedes* (p. 98)

15. (12) Apex of siphon broad, its diameter only slightly less than length of 1-S; 4 or more precratal setae....*flavescens* (p. 104)
Siphon narrow apically, diameter ½ length of 1-S or less; 2 precratal setae.. 16

16. (15) Pecten teeth evenly spaced............................ *mercurator* (p. 120)
1 or more teeth widely spaced.. 17

* Not yet found in British Columbia.

72

17. (16) Cuticle of body covered with a fur of fine spicules
($\times$ 200). Open and woodland pools—lower Fraser
Valley .... *aloponotum* (p. 78)
Cuticle smooth. Widely distributed .... *excrucians* (p. 100)

18. (11) Ventral anal papillae shorter than dorsal pair (if too short
to compare go to 20.) 19
Papillae of equal length 23

19. (18) Dorsal papillae longer than saddle. Flood or snow melt
pools .... *increpitus* (p. 114)
Dorsal papillae shorter than saddle in most specimens.
Saline or alkaline pools 20

20. (19) Setae 5 & 6-C 7 or more branched, in line with each other
at front of head. Coastal rock pools .... *togoi* (p. 142)
6-C unbranched in most specimens, in normal position
on head 21

21. (20) Seta 5-C 2 or 3-branched. Usually in alkaline pools in
dry interior .... *campestris* (p. 80)
5-C unbranched, in a few specimens 2-branched on one
side 22

22. (21) Seta 1-M as long as 5 or 6-C, 2 or 3-branched. Coastal
or dry interior .... *dorsalis* (p. 94)
1-M fine, much shorter than 5 or 6-C. Dry interior
.... *melanimon* (p. 118)

23. (18) 1 or more pecten teeth widely spaced 24
Pecten teeth even 28

24. (23) Seta 1-S inserted within pecten which extends ⅔ or more
along siphon 25
1-S at distal end of pecten which extends about ½ way
along siphon 26

25. (24) Siphon with 4 or 5 pairs of branched setae dorsally.
Woodland pools .... *provocans* (p. 126)
No dorsal setae on siphon. Usually in open pools
.... *cataphylla* (p. 86)

26. (24) Head setae 5 & 6-C unbranched; saddle almost completely surrounding segment X .... *spencerii* (p. 136)
Setae 5 & 6-C at least 4 and 2-branched respectively in
most specimens 27

27. (26) Saddle reaching ⅔ around X, ventral margin deeply incised; antennae pale, almost as long as head .... *intrudens* (p. 116)

Saddle almost completely surrounding X, margin even; antennae short, dark-pigmented in most specimens .... *vexans* (p. 144) (in part)

28. (23) Head seta 5-C 5 or more branched in most specimens, at least on one side 29

Seta 5-C less than 5-branched 31

29. (28) Setae 2 & 3-P ½ length of 1-P; 1 & 2-M of equal length, finely branched and less than ½ length of 5-C .... *canadensis* (p. 84)

2 & 3-P more than ½ length of 1-P; 1-M unbranched, as long as or longer than 5-C; 2-M much shorter and finely branched 30

30. (29) 1, 2 & 3-P of equal length, 1-P 2-branched in most specimens; about 50 uncrowded comb scales, apical spine longer than adjacent spinules (Fig. 27a) .... *pullatus* (p. 128)

1, 2 & 3-P progressively shorter, 1-P unbranched; more than 50 crowded slipper-shaped comb scales, distal spines of scales of similar length (Fig. 27b) .... *pionips* (p. 124)

31. (28) 15 or fewer thorn-shaped comb scales (Fig. 27c); setae 5 & 6-C unbranched .... *impiger* (p. 110)

16 or more comb scales 32

32. (31) Seta 1-X 1⅓ times length of saddle; 5 & 6-C 2 to 4-branched. Coastal rain forest, usually woodland pools .... *aboriginis* (p. 76)

1-X shorter than, or at most as long as saddle 33

33. (32) Saddle reaching more than ¾ around X; pecten on basal ½ or more of siphon; comb scales pointed. River floodplains .... *sticticus* (p. 138)

Saddle surrounding ⅔ or less of X; pecten on basal ⅓ to ½ of siphon 34

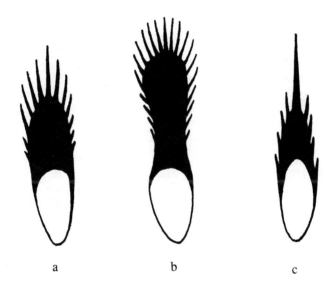

Fig. 27. Comb scales: a. *Ae. pullatus*; b. *Ae. pionips*; c. *Ae. impiger*.

34. (33) Less than 35 comb scales; larvae spread throughout
breeding area.. *implicatus* (p. 112)
More than 35 comb scales; larvae often in clusters in
breeding area.. 35
35. (34) Comb scales narrow with one or, in some scales, 2 apical
spines at least 2 × as long as adjacent spines
.... *nevadensis* (p. 122)
Comb scales broad and rounded with 8 to 10 apical
spines of similar length................................. *communis* (p. 90)

Aedes aboriginis Dyar

Aedes aboriginis Dyar, 1917. Ins. Ins. Mens. 5:99
(Latin: meaning original inhabitant)

Fig. 20a, abdomen

A large mosquito with dark unbanded tarsi; wing length 5.25–6 mm.

Female—Proboscis and palps dark-scaled. Cuticle of pedicels light brown, darker on median surface. Scutum with golden brown scales, paler around the prescutellar space but dark brown and narrower on the broad median and posterior half stripes where the dark cuticle is also apparent. Hypostigmal scale patch absent; postprocoxal present. 1 or 2 lower mesepimeral setae. Abdominal tergites dark with solid white basal bands. Wings dark-scaled. Femora dark with a few pale scales ventrally at the base. Adults are difficult to distinguish from *punctor* (woodland) and *hexodontus* (subalpine). The larvae are distinct.

Larva (Fig. 28)—Antennae spiculate, less than half length of head. Head seta 5-C 3 to 5-branched, 6-C 2 to 4-branched. Prothoracic seta 1-P 2 or 3-branched. Seta 1-M 1½ times length of 5 or 6-C (1-M barely longer than 5-C in *mercurator*). Comb of segment VIII with 25-38 scales, each with a strong median spine flanked by a number of short, strong laterals. Siphon 2½ × 1. Pecten teeth evenly spaced, ending before mid siphon. Seta 1-S long, 4 to 6-branched, inserted beyond pecten. Saddle reaching more than half way around anal segment. Seta 1-X and papillae longer than saddle.

The coastal rain forests form the typical habitat of this species. It extends from Vancouver Island to Chilliwack in the south and further north has been found near Prince Rupert and in Alaska. Hearle (1926) did not find it generally distributed in the Fraser Valley and stated that it was "neither very vicious or persisitent in its attack." More recently I found the females numerous and annoying around Burnaby Lake in late May and early June. In the same area, the larvae develop early (March–May) in temporary rain and snow pools in or near wooded areas. Within a few days of emergence, males swarmed in the evenings at the tips of broadleaf maple or alder branches, 2-3 m above the ground.

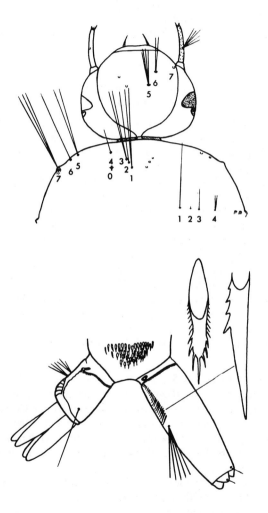

Fig. 28.   Larva, *Ae. aboriginis*.

Aedes aloponotum Dyar

Aedes aloponotum Dyar, 1917. Ins. Ins. Mens. 5:98
Aedes excrucians: of authors, not Walker
Aedes fletcheri aloponotum Hearle, 1920.
(Greek: *alopex* = fox, referring to the reddish orange colour of the notum)

Fig. 21b, claw

A large, light brown mosquito with sharp white basal bands on the abdominal tergites and tarsi; wing length 5.5–6.4 mm.

Female—Proboscis dark with a few pale scales. Pedicels with pale cuticle, except medially where it is dark and there are pale scales. Scutum predominantly golden brown scaled but with a few white scales around the margin and on the prescutellar space and the scutellum. On the scutum a median and 2 lateral rows of setae, darker than the scales, show up as 3 fine longitudinal lines (20 ×). The reddish brown cuticle is visible in rubbed specimens. Hypostigmal area bare (scaled in *riparius*). Postprocoxal area with pale scales. No lower mesepimeral setae. Scales of the abdomen much darker than those of the scutum. Tergites with basal white bands. Wings dark with scattered pale scales. Legs dark with a patch of white scales at the apices of the femora and with broad white bands on all hind tarsomeres. Fore and mid tarsomeres with narrower bands, lacking on fore tarsal segment 5 of some specimens. The shape of the tarsal claws immediately separates this species from *excrucians* (Fig. 21a & b). *Aloponotum* females are very similar to *riparius* but their distribution does not overlap in British Columbia; the male genitalia are distinct.

Larva (Fig. 29)—Head seta 5-C 2 to 5-branched, 6-C 2 to 3-branched. Thorax and abdomen covered with minute spicules giving the body a furry appearance (200 ×), (cuticle smooth in *excrucians*). Comb scales 26–37, most with a long apical and shorter subapical spines. Siphon 4½–5 × 1, pecten reaching half way along, 2 or 3 distal teeth more widely spaced than the others. Saddle reaching ¾ around anal segment. Cuticle of head and siphon pale.

Dyar described the species in 1917 from females he collected in Washington State. By 1920 he apparently concluded that it was a synonym of *fletcheri* and that year Hearle called it *Ae. fletcheri aloponotum*.

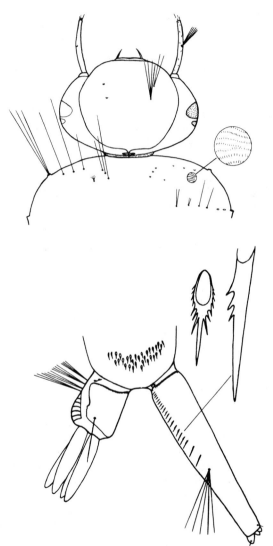

Fig. 29.   Larva, *Ae. aloponotum*.

In his survey of the Fraser Valley in 1926, however, Hearle recognized *aloponotum* as a distinct species. Later authors considered it a synonym of the better-known species, *Ae. excrucians,* until Boddy (1948) found some new taxonomic characters and redescribed it as a genuine species. Wood (1977) confirmed Hearle's identification of specimens from British Columbia.

It has been found as far east as Spokane, Wash., and west to southern Vancouver Island. I have found it in woodland in the lower Fraser Valley where it bites readily particularly in the evening and its larvae occur in woodland pools and open pools with grassy bottoms from March until May. They were associated with larvae of *aboriginis* and *cinereus* in the woods and with these species and *Cs. morsitans* in the grassy pools. *Aloponotum* larvae are paler than those of *aboriginis* and *cinereus* and, like several other species with long siphons, they lie ventral side up at the bottom of natural breeding sites or rearing pans. I have seen males at sunset, in fast irregular flight, heading for the tops of trees, 10–30 m high. They probably swarm in much the same way as *excrucians.*

Aedes campestris Dyar and Knab

> *Aedes campestris* Dyar and Knab, 1907. J.N.Y.ent.Soc.15:213
> *Aedes callithotrys* Dyar, 1920.
> (Latin: of fields, referring to its open grassland habitat)

Fig. 23a, claw

A predominantly yellow and brown species of medium size; wing length 4.3–5 mm, with indistinct pale basal and apical tarsal bands.

Female—Proboscis and palps black-scaled, pale scales intermixed basally. Pedicels brown with a few white scales. Scutum blonde, with a broad brownish median stripe and lateral stripes, narrowing at mid length. Hypostigmal area scaled. Postprocoxal scale patch prominent. Lower mesepimeral setae 2-7. Abdominal tergites II-V with paired lateral patches of black scales, surrounded by pale scales; scales on VI and VII all pale. Most tarsomeres with basal and apical silvery white bands but segments 4 and 5 of fore and 5 of mid tarsi all dark and 5 of hind tarsi mainly white. Fore tarsal claw bent beyond lateral tooth, like that of *melanimon* (Fig. 23a), lateral tooth longer than that of *dorsalis.* Most

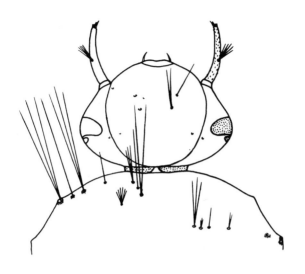

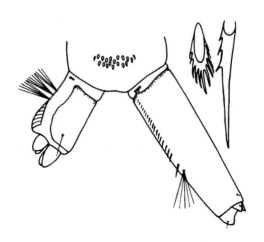

Fig. 30.   Larva, *Ae. campestris*.

wing veins with white and brown scales evenly intermixed, white predominating on R_{4+5} and the apices of M_1 and M_2 (*dorsalis* has small dark appressed scales on these veins), and vein A entirely pale scaled (as in *dorsalis*; in *melanimon* A is predominantly dark scaled). The male genitalia of the three species are distinct.

Larva (Fig. 30)—Head seta 5-C 2 to 4-branched, 6-C 1 or 2-branched. Seta 1-M 2 or 3-branched and longer than 5 or 6-C. Comb of VIII with 19–33 scales in a ragged triangular patch, median spine(s) of most scales somewhat longer than adjacent spines (spines of even length in *dorsalis*). Siphon 3×1, pecten extending about ⅔ along it; distal tooth stouter and more widely spaced than others in most specimens (pecten teeth even in *dorsalis*). 1-S inserted beyond pecten. Saddle reaching ⅔ around anal segment. Papillae short and bud-like, ventral pair shorter than dorsal. Seta 1-X shorter than saddle.

In British Columbia this univoltine species appears to be confined to the dry interior and the Cariboo Parklands where Hearle (1932) found it to be one of the dominant mosquito pests in the Chilcotin. It breeds in somewhat alkaline pools, rich in organic matter, as soon as the snow has melted. Gibson (1933) found that it could fly distances of at least 6 miles and in 1937 he described swarms of *campestris* females attacking workmen repairing roofs at Tranquille, even during the extreme heat of midday. In the United States it is reported to breed in flooded grasslands, and is sometimes associated with *Ae. vexans*. The females bite when disturbed at any time of day. It is a pest of humans and sometimes cattle. McLintock *et al.* (1970) have found this species occasionally infected with WEE virus, but it probably plays a minor role in spreading disease, compared with *Cx. tarsalis* and *Cs. inornata*.

Control of this species, along with its near relatives *dorsalis* and *melanimon,* presents several problems. It is undesirable to use larvicides where cattle are grazing, yet because these species have a wide flight range it is uneconomic to attempt to control the adults. Where they are serious pests, the possibility of killing the larvae with new growth regulators and highly selective bacterial toxins should be investigated.

Aedes canadensis (Theobald)

Culex canadensis Theobald, 1901, Mon.Culic. 2:3
(Latin: of Canada)

A small, dark brown species with conspicuous white basal and apical tarsal bands; wing length 3–4 mm.

Female—Proboscis dark-scaled. Palps with a few white scales in some specimens. Pedicels dark brown with darker scales on median surface. Scutum brown-scaled, reddish brown when rubbed. Margins of scutum with paler yellowish brown scales and pale posterior half stripes in some specimens. No hypostigmal or postprocoxal scale patch. No lower mesepimeral setae. Abdomen dark-scaled with incomplete pale basal bands, forming lateral triangular patches in most specimens. Most tarsomeres with pale basal and apical bands of equal length (apical bands 4 or more times width of basal bands in *sierrensis*). Tarsomere 5 of hind leg entirely white-scaled. Wings dark scaled.

Larva (Fig. 31)—Antennae spiculate, apical half pigmented. Head setae 5-C 4 to 9-branched, 6-C 3 to 6-branched. Seta 1-M short, about same length as 2-M (1-M longer than 2-M in *pullatus* and *pionips*). 25–40 comb scales in an irregular patch. Siphon 3×1, pecten teeth evenly spaced along basal ⅓. Seta 1-S 5-branched, inserted just distal to pecten. 1-X shorter than, and papillae longer than, saddle.

Ae. canadensis is a typical woodland species breeding in temporary pools. Adults have been found from May to September and although most of the eggs are laid in sites that fill with melted snow in early spring, others may be laid in sites that are submerged by later spring or summer rainfall. Brust (1968) found that, although most eggs overwinter, about 30% will hatch the year they are laid so that there may be a partial 2nd generation. Males have been seen, after sunset, swarming between dwarf spruces in swampy ground (Dyar 1919). *Ae. canadensis* has been collected along the Fraser Valley at least as far as Prince George, in the Okanagan and Kootenays and as far north as Lower Post. It is not generally common enough to be a pest but is a persistent biter in woodland, attacking low.

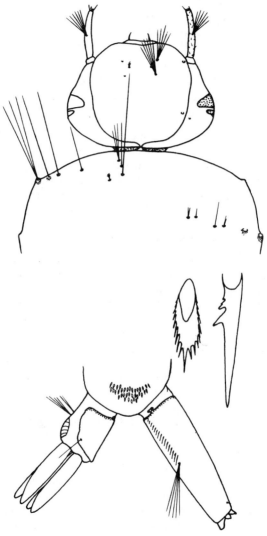

Fig. 31. Larva, *Ae. canadensis*.

Aedes cataphylla Dyar

Aedes cataphylla Dyar, 1916. Ins. Ins. Mens. 4:86
Aedes prodotes Dyar, 1917.
Aedes pacificensis Hearle, 1927.

(Greek: *cata* = downward, *phylla* = leaf, referring to Fallen Leaf in California, where Dyar first collected it)

A medium-sized species with unbanded tarsi; wing length 3.7–4.5 mm.

Female—Proboscis dark with scattered light scales basally. Palps dark, speckled with white scales. Pedicels dark brown with white scales on median and dorsal surfaces. Scutum with narrow golden scales medially, shading to grayish at margins. Postprocoxal scale patch present (absent in *pullatus*); hypostigmal patch present in most specimens. Lower mesepimeral setae 2-7. Abdomen black, tergites with basal white bands. Legs dark with scattered pale scales. Tarsi mainly black. Wings dark-scaled, but with a line of pale scales at the base of vein C and scattered pale scales at the base of Sc and R.

Larva (Fig. 32)—Head setae 5 and 6-C unbranched in most specimens. 10–25 thorn-shaped comb scales in an irregular double row or patch. Siphon about 3 × 1; pecten with 3–5 teeth more widely spaced, reaching nearly to apex; 1-S inserted before mid length. Saddle reaching about ⅔ around anal segment. 1-X thin and shorter than saddle.

This species occurs throughout the Province from coastal islands to high mountains and from the 49th to 60th parallel. Hearle (1927c) thought he had found a new species, *pacificensis,* when he collected it on Discovery Island, noting a thick column of males swarming on a thinly wooded ridge near a salt marsh. Not very common in the Fraser Valley, it is one of the predominant species of the dry interior grasslands. Hearle (1932) found it, with *campestris,* the main pest in the Chilcotin. Most commonly it breeds in open grassy snow melt pools, but is also found in forests and is very abundant in river flood pools in the Rocky Mountain foothills. It is a strong flier, bites in broad daylight and is aggressive. Hearle observed it near Kamloops attacking livestock in some numbers in May and noted that *cataphylla* was a very productive breeder. This impression was verified by studies of Carpenter & Nielsen (1965) who found that one female could mature 5 batches of eggs in one season.

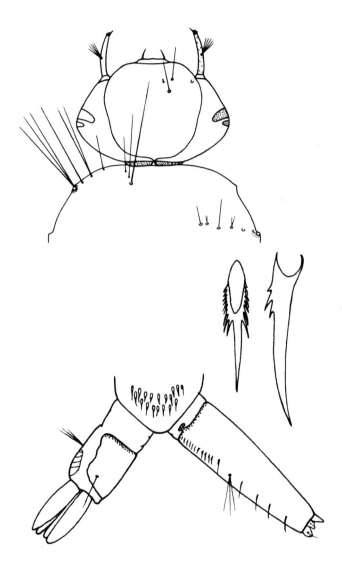

Fig. 32.   Larva, *Ae. cataphylla*.

Controlling mosquitoes in pasture has always been a problem. Organchloride insecticides tend to accumulate in milk and fat, and carbamates and organophosphates, although not cumulative, are toxic to mammals. New bacterial insecticides, which are selective for mosquitoes, may prove to be an acceptable means of controlling larvae. Cattle can be protected from the adults with repellents and selectively toxic insecticides.

Aedes cinereus Meigen

> *Aedes cinereus* Meigen, 1818. Syst. Beschr. Zweifl. Ins. 1:13
> *Aedes fuscus* Osten Sacken, 1877.
> (Latin: ashy, probably referring to the drab colour of the adult)
>
> Fig. 24a, abdomen

A small to very small, dark mosquito with unbanded tarsi; wing length 3.2–3.8 mm. Abdomen with lateral silvery white stripes. In British Columbia, males of this species are unique in having short palps resembling those of the females.

Female—Proboscis and palps dark-scaled. Pedicels brown, median surface darker. Behind the eyes are two distinctive patches of dark appressed scales. Scutum covered with reddish brown scales. No hypostigmal or postprocoxal scale patch or lower mesepimeral setae. Abdominal tergites dark medially in all specimens examined from the Lower Mainland; some specimens from the interior have distinct pale basal bands. From the side (in all specimens) there is a crisp silvery lateral stripe running the length of the abdomen (Fig. 24a). Sternites covered with silvery white scales. Legs and wing scales dark.

Larva (Fig. 33)—Head setae 5-C 5 to 9-branched and 6-C 4 to 8-branched, in line with 7-C at the base of the antenna. Comb with 9–16 thorn-shaped scales in a ragged row. Siphon 4×1, pecten reaching beyond mid length, 2 or 3 teeth widely spaced. 1-S small, inserted beyond pecten. Saddle reaching ⅔ to ¾ around anal segment. 1-X 2-branched, shorter than saddle.

This species has been recorded from every part of the Province. It is found in or close to woodland and has a somewhat restricted flight range. It hatches equally well in open or shaded flood water, rain pools or swamps. Its biting habits are varied and it may be present but harmless or

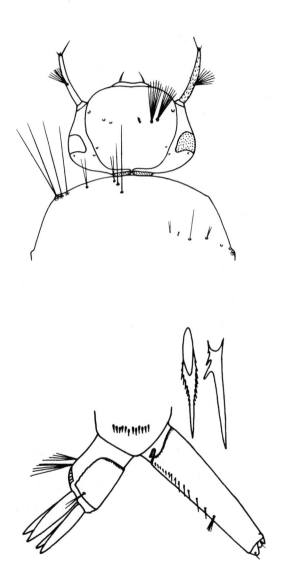

Fig. 33. Larva, *Ae. cinereus*.

at other times, may attack persistently. Near Burnaby Lake, open grassy pools were thick with larvae in April and May. In late May and early June males swarmed, just after sunset, over patches of horsetails and females bit only when disturbed. Specimens I collected in the dry interior, however, bit persistently in bright sunlight. Although it may be locally common it is not generally abundant and cannot be considered a major pest.

Aedes communis (Degeer)

> *Culex communis* Degeer, 1776. Mem.des Ins. 6:316
> *Culex lazarensis* Felt & Young, 1904.
> (Latin: common; Dyar noted that this species is abundant wherever it is found)

A medium-sized species with dark unbanded tarsi; wing length 4.5–5 mm.

Female—Proboscis with dark brown scales, palps sprinkled with white scales. Cuticle of pedicels brown, white-scaled on median surface. Vertex with yellow erect forked scales, some brown ones intermixed. Scutum usually clad in yellowish scales, with a dark brown median stripe divided by a narrow line of yellow scales and with lateral half-stripes, not always well defined. Hypostigmal and postprocoxal scale patches absent (postprocoxal area scaled in the similar *punctor* and *pionips* females). Lower mesepimeral setae 2–6. Abdominal tergites with basal creamy white bands, widening laterally. Legs dark. Wings dark-scaled, with a small patch of white scales at base of C in some specimens.

Larva (Fig. 34)—Head setae 5 & 6-C unbranched, 5-C 2-branched in a few specimens. 30–70 evenly-fringed comb scales in a triangular patch. Siphon 2½–3 × 1. Pecten even, reaching to about mid siphon. 1-S many-branched, inserted beyond pecten. Saddle reaching more than half way around anal segment. 1-X much shorter than saddle. Papillae long and pointed.

The biology of this species was confusing until 1973 when Ellis and Brust confirmed suspicions that it was, in fact, a combination of 3 closely related species. *Ae. communis* occurs in British Columbia and the very similar but non-biting species, *churchillensis* Ellis and Brust, in Alberta, a few kilometres from our northeastern boundary. The third sibling species, *nevadensis,* Chapman and Barr, bites in mountainous regions of

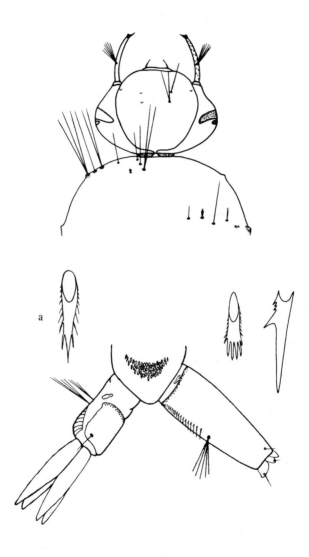

Fig. 34.   Larva, *Ae. communis* (a = comb scale).

Washington and Idaho and has recently been found on the southern margin of the Province.

Observations in Alberta indicate that *communis* is diurnal in habit, being most active in early morning and late afternoon (Happold 1965). In British Columbia it bites fiercely at dawn and dusk in the open and at any time of the day in the woods. It has been recorded across the Province and breeds mainly in shaded pools. Although most commonly found at medium altitudes, it can be found in cottonwood bottoms along with *sticticus*. Dyar (1920) found it one of the commonest species in the mountains but dominant down to tide level in the Skeena Valley. The larvae appear very early in spring. In Denmark, they have been known to hatch in midwinter when a brief warm spell thawed out sunny margins of pools. With the resumption of normal cold weather the pools froze over for another 3 months after which the larvae were able to continue their development (Wesenberg-Lund 1921). Adults are usually found near the breeding site but on occasion have been reported to disperse more than 20 kilometres (Hocking 1953). Although it is a fierce biter, it is not considered a major pest in British Columbia.

Aedes diantaeus Howard, Dyar & Knab

> *Aedes diantaeus* Howard, Dyar & Knab, 1917. Mosq.N.and Cent.Amer.and W.I. 4:758
> (Greek: *diantaios* = extending throughout, but it is not clear from the description to what this referred)

Figs. 19a, tarsus; 24b, abdomen

A medium-sized species with dark unbanded tarsi and incomplete bands on abdominal tergites; wing length 4–4.5 mm.

Female—Proboscis and palps dark-scaled. Pedicels light brown laterally, median surface darker with short dark setae. Scutum with dark cuticle and golden yellow scales. The median brown stripe is divided longitudinally by a line of yellowish scales in some specimens. Hypostigmal and postprocoxal scale patches absent. Lower mesepimeral setae lacking, except in a very few specimens where 1 or at most 2 may be present. Abdominal tergites dark brown with baso-lateral triangular white patches, sometimes connected by a narrow white bar on posterior segments. Legs black with bronzy reflections. Wing scales dark brown.

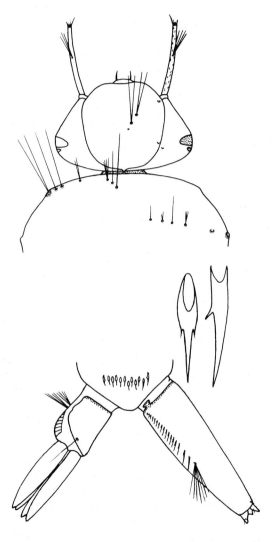

Fig. 35. Larva, *Ae. diantaeus*.

Larva (Fig. 35)—Antennae long, slender and straight; relatively much longer than those of our other aedines. Head setae 5-C and 6-C 2 or 3-branched. 8–12 thorn-shaped comb scales in an irregular row. Siphon slender, $3\frac{1}{2}$–4 × 1, pecten reaching mid siphon, 1 to 3 teeth widely spaced. 1-S 7 to 9-branched, inserted beyond pecten. Saddle reaching ¾ to almost completely around anal segment.

Ae. diantaeus is rare in British Columbia; most specimens have been collected from northern coast forest. Dyar (1920) found it "not uncommon" in the Skeena Valley and observed that the males did not swarm but were attracted to warm-blooded animals and seized females as they approached to bite. The females are active biters at all times of day. The larvae inhabit cold pools in deep forest and emerge early in the year.

Aedes dorsalis (Meigen)

Culex dorsalis Meigen, 1830. Syst.Besch.Bek.Eur.Zwei.Ins. 6:242
Culex curriei Coquillett, 1901.

(Latin: of the back, referring to the markings on the scutum and abdominal tergites)

Figs 19c, tarsus; 22b, katepisternum; 23b, claw

A medium-sized, fawn-coloured species, yellower on the coast, with indistinct pale basal and apical tarsal bands; wings length 4–4.5 mm.

Female—Palps and base of proboscis speckled with white scales, tip of palp entirely dark. Pedicels brown, white-scaled on median and dorsal surfaces. Scutum with fawn scales, a median stripe of narrow brown scales and, in some specimens, brown posterior half-stripes. The appearance of the median stripe varies across the continent. It is divided in the form found in British Columbia which used to be considered a separate species, *curriei*. Scales around the margin of the scutum and on the pleuron are whitish in specimens from the interior and yellowish in those on the coast, as they are in coastal California (Bohart & Washino 1978). Hypostigmal and postprocoxal patches many-scaled. Lower mesepimeral setae 2–6. Pleural scales all narrow. Abdominal tergites variable, most specimens have basal white bands widening at the sides and a white median stripe, leaving paired black patches apically on each segment, except I, VII and VIII which are almost entirely white. Femora

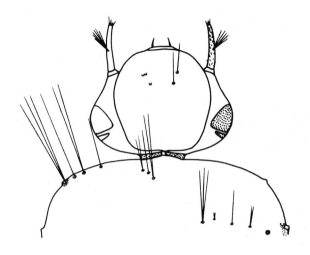

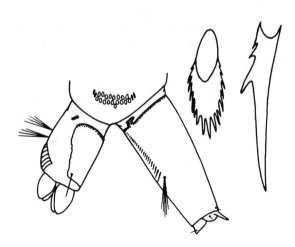

Fig. 36.   Larva, *Ae. dorsalis*.

and tibiae brown, speckled white and dark. Most tarsomeres dark with pale bands apically and basally. Wings with mingled light and dark scales. Dark scales predominate on veins C, R_1 and R_{4+5} and the apices of M_1 and M_2, the dark scales small and appressed on the last three veins. The wings are almost entirely dark in some specimens and, in this case, their claws will have to be examined to separate them from *melanimon* (Figs. 23a & b). The male genitalia are distinct.

Larva (Fig. 36)—Head setae 5 and 6-C unbranched. 20–30 ovoid comb scales in a patch, apical spines of equal length. Siphon about 3×1, pecten evenly spaced reaching to about mid siphon, 1-S inserted just beyond pecten. Saddle reaching little more than half way around anal segment. Papillae short and blunt, ventral pair shorter than dorsal.

This mosquito lives a double life in British Columbia. At the coast it is our principal salt-marsh breeder and I have found a few larvae in rock pools with *Ae. togoi* and *Cs. incidens*. In the Fraser delta it is not usually found more than 1 or 2 kilometres inland. It is a more or less continuous breeder in the summer, as successive spring tides flood the marshes. It can, in consequence, be a pest on nearby beaches. Males can be seen at sunset swarming over bushes and tall herbs. At the Tsawwassen salt marsh they seem to favour patches of yellow lupin as swarm markers.

On the interior plateau *dorsalis* thrives, not only in saline swamps and pools, but also in fresh water such as irrigation seepages. It breeds in open sunny habitats and is typically a mosquito of the grasslands where its flight range may extend for many miles. The females are vicious biters by day or night. WEE virus has been isolated from low percentages of this species in Saskatchewan (McLintock *et al.*1970).

The species is controlled in the same way as *campestris*.

Aedes euedes Howard, Dyar & Knab

Aedes euedes Howard, Dyar & Knab, 1917. Mosq.N.and
Cent.Amer.and W.I. 4:714
(Greek: *eueides* = well-shaped or comely)

Fig. 21d, claw

A large species with pale basal bands on the tarsi; wing length 5.2–5.5 mm.

Female—Proboscis liberally sprinkled with white scales; from the side, it appears to have a transverse white band at mid length. Palps dark with scattered pale scales at the bases of the segments. Pedicels pale-scaled. Scutum reddish brown with narrow white lines on either side of an indistinct median stripe; a narrow, central, darker line on the cuticle shows through the scales. Anterior to the prescutellar space lateral patches of pale scales lie alongside the median stripe. Lower mesepimeral setae and hypostigmal scale patch absent. Postprocoxal patch of pale scales present. Abdominal tergites with basal white bands. Legs with scattered pale scales. The females are very similar to those of *excrucians* and *aloponotum*. They can be separated by the shape of the tarsal claws (Figs. 21a, b & d). Wings dark with many scattered pale scales.

Larva (Fig. 37)—Head setae 5 and 6-C 2-branched in most specimens. 10–20 long-spined comb scales in a ragged row. Siphon 3½–4 × 1, pecten reaching more than half way along it, 2 or 3 teeth unevenly spaced. 1-S inserted just distal to last tooth. (In *aloponotum* and *excrucians,* pecten may have 1 or 2 widely spaced teeth but does not reach mid siphon near which 1-S is inserted). Saddle reaching ⅔ or more around anal segment. Papillae brownish in some specimens, much longer than anal segment.

Adults of this species are easily confused with *excrucians,* because the females and the male genitalia are almost identical. On the other hand, the larvae can be misidentified as *riparius* if the keys of Rempel (1950) or Curtis (1967a) are used. I have seen larvae and adults in collections from northern forest, the Cariboo, Okanagan and Lower Fraser Valley and it probably occurs throughout the Province. *Ae. euedes* is known to attack man readily but is unlikely to be found in sufficient numbers to be considered a pest in British Columbia.

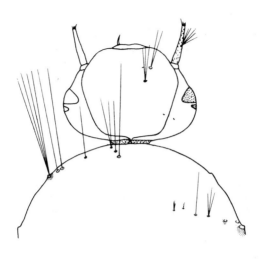

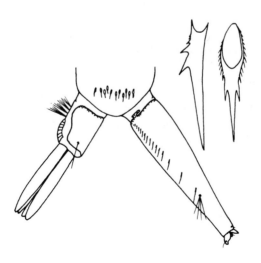

Fig. 37. Larva, *Ae. euedes*.

Aedes excrucians (Walker)

Culex excrucians Walker, 1856. Ins.Saund.Dipt. p.429
(Latin: tormenting, probably referring to its biting habits)

Figs. 19b, tarsus; 21a, claw

A medium to large species with basally banded tarsi and distinctive claws; wing length 5 mm.

Female—Proboscis predominantly dark-scaled. Pedicels mostly white-scaled. Palps with pale basal bands. Scutum with a variable pattern of brown and white scales, the broad brown median stripe sometimes divided longitudinally. Hypostigmal scale patch absent, postprocoxal present. Lower mesepimeral setae absent, or with 1 in a few specimens. Abdominal tergites with pale basal bands and scattered pale scales, more numerous on posterior segments. Basal white bands broad on hind tarsi, narrower on mid and fore tarsi. Fore tarsal claw distinctive (Fig. 21a). Wings mainly dark scaled with scattered pale scales. Adults from the north of the Province are darker, overall, than those from the south.

Larva (Fig. 38)—Head seta 5-C 2 or 3-branched, 6-C 1 or 2-branched. 15–34 thorn-shaped comb scales in a patch. Siphon slender, 4×1; pecten not reaching mid length, 1 or 2 distal teeth widely spaced. Saddle reaching about ¾ around anal segment. Papillae long and pointed.

This holarctic species is found locally throughout the Province, mainly in woodland. In the dry interior, adults are also active in open grassland. The larvae breed in a wide variety of temporary pools. Adults generally appear somewhat later than other species and survive well into late summer. The females are fierce biters. It is a major pest species in central Alberta (Graham 1969), but is less numerous and of minor importance in British Columbia.

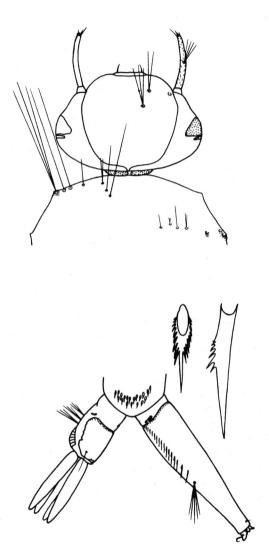

Fig. 38.   Larva, *Ae. excrucians*.

Aedes fitchii (Felt & Young)

Culex fitchii Felt & Young, 1904. Science 20:312
(Named after Asa Fitch, an early collector in New York State)

Fig. 21c, claw

A medium-sized species with pale basal bands on the tarsi; wing length 4.5–5 mm.

Female—Proboscis predominantly dark-scaled. Pedicels yellow, median surface darker and white-scaled. Scutum with yellowish-white scales laterally and a broad single or double median stripe of narrow chocolate-brown scales. Hypostigmal area bare in all specimens I have examined from the Province. Postprocoxal area scaled. Lower mesepimeral setae 0–2, rarely 3 or 4. This variability causes *fitchii* to key out in 2 places. Abdominal tergites with distinct pale basal bands and a few additional scattered white scales in some specimens. Hind tarsomeres with broad white basal bands, narrower on fore and mid tarsi. Wings dark-scaled with a scattering of pale ones.

Larva (Fig. 39)—Head seta 5-C 2 to 4-branched, longer than 6-C which is 1 to 3-branched. Up to 30 comb scales in a patch, but their number and shape is extremely variable (Barr 1958). In the specimens I have examined from British Columbia they are long-spined and range from 11–15 in number. Siphon long and slender, more than 4×1; pecten not reaching mid length, teeth evenly spaced. 1-S long, inserted about mid siphon. Saddle reaching about ⅔ around anal segment. Papillae long and pointed.

This species has been found throughout the Province from Vancouver Island to the Rockies and north to Atlin. It is a snow pool breeder, often associated with *increpitus,* and commonly occurs in open woods or the transition area between forest and grassland. It is an aggressive biter and is one of the main pest mosquitoes of the southern interior. Frequently found at high altitudes, it can be a nuisance up to 1500 m.

In recreational areas it may be possible to control larvae where the breeding sites have been identified but it is probably more practical for campers, hunters and fisherman to use repellents or repellent clothing.

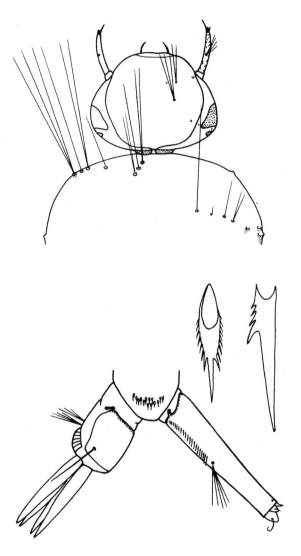

Fig. 39. Larva, *Ae. fitchii*.

103

Aedes flavescens (Müller)

Culex flavescens Müller, 1764. Fauna.Ins.Fried. p. 87
Culex fletcheri Coquillett, 1902.
(Latin: yellowish, referring to its overall colour)

Fig. 20b, abdomen

A large, dull-yellow species, with pale basal bands on the tarsi; wing length 5.5–6 mm.

Female—Proboscis and palps dark brown with scattered yellowish scales. Pedicels brown with dark setae and yellow scales on darker median surface. Scutum yellowish-brown with a broad, darker brown, median stripe. Area around and below spiracle almost entirely covered with scales. No lower mesepimeral setae. Abdomen unbanded, dorsum covered with yellowish scales (Fig. 20b). Tarsomeres dark, with wide yellowish basal bands. Wing scales mainly yellow, with scattered brown ones.

Larva (Fig. 40)—Head seta 5-C 2 to 5-branched, 6-C 2 or 3-branched. 20–40 thorn-shaped comb scales in a patch. Siphon $3\frac{1}{2}$ to 4×1, pecten on basal $\frac{2}{5}$, evenly spaced or with 1 or 2 distal teeth widely spaced. Anal segment with 4 precratal setae; 1-X shorter than saddle which reaches $\frac{2}{3}$ around segment. Papillae as long as anal segment in most specimens.

This species, although not common in British Columbia, has been collected at widely separated points. It is normally a mosquito of open grassland, breeding in alkaline pools, but oddly enough the first provincial record of the species was a capture high on Mt. Cheam (Hearle 1926). There is an unconfirmed record of *flavescens* from Richmond, so it may also inhabit our coastal salt marshes as it does in Alaska (Gjullin *et al.* 1961). The full grown larvae are very large and it is one of the latest species to mature. In June and July compact swarms of 60 or 70 males form over low vegetation at dusk (Hearle 1929). Females bite viciously, feeding readily on birds, horses, cattle and man, but are rarely sufficiently numerous to be a pest in this Province. WEE virus has been isolated from a few Saskatchewan specimens (McLintock *et al.* 1970).

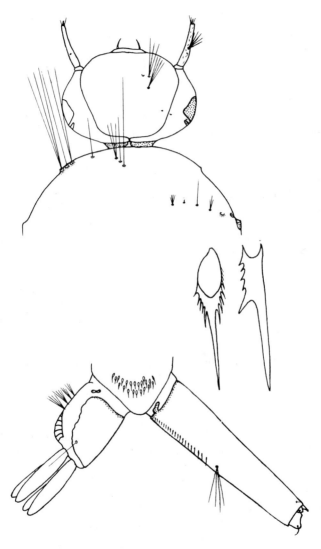

Fig. 40.   Larva, *Ae. flavescens*.

Aedes hendersoni Cockerell

Aedes triseriatus var. *hendersoni* Cockerell, 1918. J.Econ.Ent. 11:199

(named after Professor Junius Henderson who collected the mosquito in Colorado)

A small mosquito that breeds in tree-holes, with a distinctively marked scutum and dark unbanded tarsi; wing length 3.5–4 mm.

Female—Proboscis and palps black. Pedicels brown with fine dark setae on median surface. Anterior and anterolateral margins of scutum with silvery white rounded scales. A broad brown stripe medially with a partial or complete narrow central white stripe. A few white scales at the anterior of the prescutellar space which is flanked by long golden setae. No postprocoxal or hypostigmal scale patch or lower mesepimeral setae. Abdominal tergites black, with basolateral patches of white scales. Femora with small apical patches of pale scales. Hind tarsal claw with no lateral tooth (*sierrensis* and a few specimens of *vexans* also lack this tooth). Wing veins dark-scaled.

Larva (Fig. 41)—Antennae smooth, 1-A unbranched (as in *sierrensis,* the other tree-hole species in British Columbia). Head seta 5-C unbranched, 6-C 2 to 4-branched. 8–12 long blunt comb scales in an irregular row. Siphon 3×1, not markedly tapered, pecten almost reaching mid length. 1-S 2 or 3-branched, inserted at or just beyond mid siphon. Saddle reaching less than half way around anal segment. 1-X shorter than saddle, 2 to 3-branched, inserted on apical margin of saddle or on adjacent unsclerotised cuticle. Papillae large and bluntly rounded and swimming setae sparse (again, as in *sierrensis*).

This species breeds in the water-filled rot cavities of trees in southern Canada and most of the United States east of the Great Divide. It is uncommon in the Province with confirmed records of an adult from Vernon which according to Wood (personal communication) Curtis (1967a) had misidentified as *triseriatus,* a similar treehole species restricted to the east, and of a breeding population in cottonwoods near Kootenay Lake (Arnell & Nielsen 1972). Little is known of its biology; eggs may be laid just above the water level of suitable rot cavities and they may hatch after rain. It probably overwinters as an egg in the northern part of its range. It bites man readily but is not a pest in British Columbia.

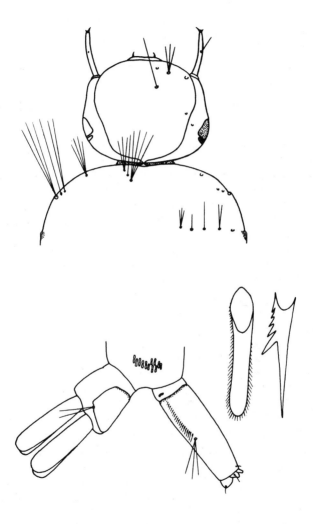

Fig. 41.   Larva, *Ae. hendersoni*.

Aedes hexodontus Dyar

Aedes hexodontus Dyar, 1916. Ins.Ins.Mens. 4:83
Aedes cyclocerculus Dyar, 1920.
Aedes leuconotips Dyar, 1920.
(Greek: six-toothed, referring to the typical number of comb scales in the larva)

A small to medium-sized species with dark tarsi; wing length 3.7–4.5 mm.

Female—Proboscis and palps dark. Cuticle of pedicels dark with pale scales. Scutum yellowish brown, paler at lateral margins, with a broad, single or double, dark brown median stripe; dark postero-lateral half stripes in some specimens. Prescutellar space paler yellow. Postprocoxal scale patch marked, hypostigmal area bare. Lower mesepimeral setae 1–3. Abdominal tergites with basal white bands. Femora, tibiae and basal tarsal segments dark, sprinkled with pale scales, distal segments entirely dark. Wing dark-scaled, with a patch of white scales at base of C (white patch smaller or absent in *punctor*). It is difficult to separate the adults from those of *aboriginis* and *punctor*.

Larva (Fig. 42)—Head setae 5 & 6-C 1 to 3-branched. 5 to 9, most commonly 6, long thorn-shaped comb scales in a row (a patch of 25 to 38 scales in *aboriginis*). Pecten reaching half way along siphon, teeth evenly spaced. Saddle surrounding anal segment (not surrounding it in *aboriginis*). Papillae long and tapered. Knight (1951) and Kalpage & Brust (1968) separated the larvae from those of *punctor* by the number and size of the comb scales which are usually fewer (5–9) and longer (more than 0.1 mm, or about same length as distal pecten tooth) in *hexodontus* and more numerous (10–21) and smaller (averaging 0.08 mm, or shorter than distal 3 or 4 pecten teeth) in *punctor*.

One of the most troublesome mosquitoes of the northern tundra, *hexodontus* extends its range down the Cordillera and out to the northern coast. Dyar's synonyms, *cyclocerculus* and *leuconotips,* were both described from specimens collected near Prince Rupert. I have found it in the southern part of both the Coast and Cascade ranges at altitudes over 1000 m and it may therefore be widespread in mountainous parts of the Province. Males were found swarming in the Kootenays, low down, in

108

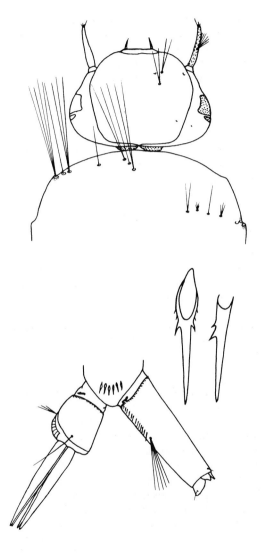

Fig. 42. Larva, *Ae. hexodontus*.

the lee of juniper bushes. In Mt. Seymour and in Manning Provincial Parks larvae were abundant in open pools on the alpine meadows and the adults bit avidly throughout the day.

Rather than attempting to control *hexodontus* it is probably more practical to advise summer visitors to these areas to use repellents.

Aedes impiger (Walker)

Culex impiger Walker, 1848. List.Dipt.Brit.Mus. 1:6
Aedes nearcticus Dyar, 1919.
(Latin: diligent or active)

Fig. 25a, claw

A small, dark, "hairy" mosquito with unbanded tarsi; wing length 3.3–4.2 mm.

Female—Proboscis and palps dark. Pedicels dark, pale-scaled on dorsal and median surface. Scutum with brown scales medially, anterior and lateral margins with yellowish scales. Numerous long black setae on the scutum and postpronotum give this mosquito a hairy appearance. Postprocoxal scale patch present, hypostigmal absent. Lower mesepimeral setae 3–8. Abdominal tergites with broad white basal bands. Tarsi black. Claw more sharply bent than that of the similar species, *nigripes* (Figs. 25a & b). Wings dark-scaled with a light patch at the bases of C and R.

Larva (Fig. 43)—Head setae 5 and 6-C long and unbranched. 10–15 thorn-shaped comb scales in a straggling double row. Siphon 3×1, pecten evenly spaced on basal third. 1-S many-branched, inserted at or before mid siphon. Saddle reaching about half way around anal segment. Papillae usually long and pointed.

Most early records of *nearcticus* Dyar will be found to refer to *impiger*, whereas some of the early *impiger* records apply to *implicatus*.

One of the two major mosquito pests of the high arctic, *impiger* is found at increasingly higher elevations in the Rocky Mountains as far south as Colorado (Carpenter & La Casse 1955).

It has been taken at Cranbrook and Hearle (1927d) found it in several localities in Rocky Mountain Park. He observed that the larvae were

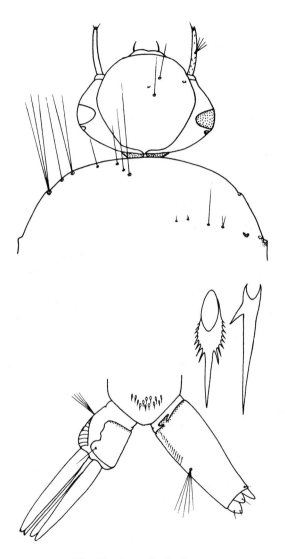

Fig. 43.   Larva, *Ae. impiger.*

numerous in pools, at or above 7,000′ (2100 m), along with those of *pullatus* and *alaskaensis*. *Impiger* probably occurs wherever there are arctic-alpine conditions in the Province.

Aedes implicatus Vockeroth

> *Aedes implicatus* Vockeroth, 1954. Can.Ent. 86:110
> *Aedes impiger,* of authors, not Walker.
> (Latin: confused, referring to the taxonomic confusion of this species with *impiger* = *nearcticus*)

Fig. 26a, katepisternum

A small species with dark, unbanded tarsi; wing length 3.5–4.3 mm.

Female—Proboscis and palps dark-scaled. Scales on pedical mostly pale. Scutum with a broad brown median stripe or paired stripes. Margins and prescutellar space greyish white. Postprocoxal scale patch present, hypostigmal area sparsely scaled in some specimens. Lower mesepimeral setae 1–3. Abdominal tergites with basal white bands. Femora and tibiae with many white scales. Tarsi dark with a few pale scales on segment 1. Wings dark-scaled with a white patch at base of C.

Larva (Fig. 44)—Head capsule dark, seta 5-C 1 or 2-branched, 6-C unbranched. 17–25 ovoid or slipper-shaped comb scales in a patch. Siphon about 3 × 1, pecten teeth evenly spaced, not reaching mid siphon, at which 1-S is inserted. Saddle reaching about ¾ around anal segment. Papillae long and pointed.

Records of this species, based on keys published before 1954 will be under the name of *impiger* Dyar (Vockeroth 1954). Such records cover most of the Province east of the coast range. It has, however, been found breeding in coastal marshes in Alaska and may yet be taken on our coast. It is a woodland mosquito which emerges early in the year. It breeds in temporary snow or rain pools. It bites vigorously in shaded situations during the day but is not common enough to be a pest.

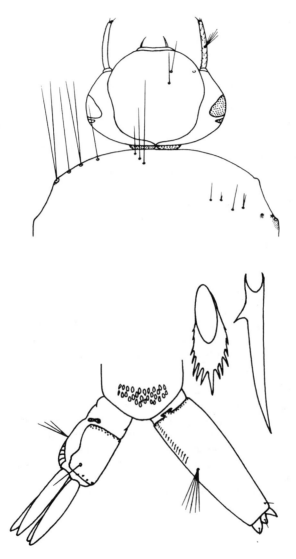

Fig. 44.   Larva, *Ae. implicatus*.

Aedes increpitus Dyar

Aedes increpitus Dyar, 1916. Ins.Ins.Mens. 4:87
Aedes mutatus Dyar, 1919.
Aedes hewitti Hearle, 1923.
(Latin: to call loudly, probably referring to its whine)

A small to medium-sized species with banded tarsi; wing length 4.0–4.5 mm.

Female—Proboscis dark. Palps mainly dark, the 2 apical segments with narrow white basal bands. Pedicels brown, sparsely white-scaled on darker median surface. Scutum with a broad brown median stripe, divided by a narrow line of white scales in most specimens, and bordered by a mixture of brown and pale scales. Postprocoxal scale patch present, hypostigmal absent. Lower mesepimeral setae 1–5. Abdominal tergites black with white basal bands widening laterally. Tarsomeres with pale basal bands, broad on hind, narrower on fore and mid tarsi. Wings brown-scaled with scattered white scales intermixed along anterior margin.

Larva (Fig. 45)—Head setae variable, 5-C 2 or 3-branched and 6-C 1 or 2-branched in most specimens. 20–40 ovoid comb scales in a patch. Siphon 3×1, pecten evenly spaced on basal ⅖. 1-S many-branched, inserted beyond pecten. Saddle reaching about ¾ around anal segment, strongly spiculate towards apex. Papillae long and pointed, dorsal pair longer than ventral.

This species is widespread and numerous in British Columbia, at the coast and throughout the interior, up to moderate altitudes. Hearle described the synonym, *hewitti,* from specimens found at Yale where males were feeding on white *Spiraea* at dusk (1923a). The larvae can be found in flood waters, irrigation seepage and rain or snow melt pools. It bites eagerly and causes great annoyance in woods and shaded locations. It can be a serious pest of cattle.

Controls should be applied to the larval breeding sites when they have been located.

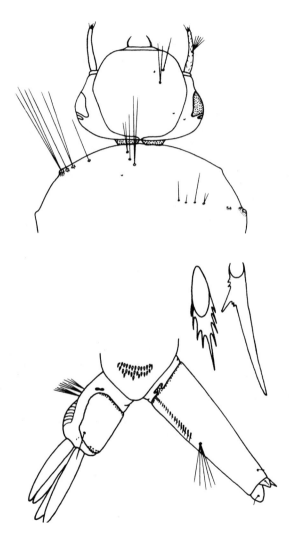

Fig. 45. Larva, *Ae. increpitus*.

Aedes intrudens Dyar

Aedes intrudens Dyar, 1919. Ins.Ins.Mens. 7:23
(Latin: intruding, referring to Dyar's observation that it was the only woodland mosquito that entered buildings)

A small to medium-sized mosquito with dark unbanded tarsi; wing length 4.0–4.2 mm.

Female—Proboscis and palps dark, palps with a sprinkling of white scales. Pedicels yellowish laterally, shading to brown medially. Scutum mainly brown-scaled, sometimes paler towards the margins. No postprocoxal scale patch, hypostigmal area scaled in some specimens. Lower mesepimeral setae 1–5. Abdominal tergites with broad white basal bands, widening laterally. Tarsi dark-scaled with a sprinkling of pale scales on segment 1. Wing scales dark brown, a few pale scales at base of C in some specimens.

Larva (Fig. 46)—Antennae slender, longer than those of aedines other than *diantaeus*. Head seta 5-C 3 or 4-branched, 6-C 2 or 3-branched. 10–16 thorn-shaped comb scales in a ragged double row. Siphon tapered, about 3×1, pecten on basal half, 1 or more distal teeth widely spaced. 1-S inserted alongside distal tooth in many specimens. Saddle reaching about ¾ around anal segment, its ventral margin deeply indented. Papillae long and pointed.

This is a typical woodland mosquito, a vicious biter by day and night, and a great nuisance when encountered. Fortunately it is not one of our commoner species. It has been found scattered throughout the Province, predominantly in the dry interior, but as far west as Vancouver Island and north to Fort Nelson. The larvae breed in woodland, bogs and snow pools. Since Dyar's early observations, several entomologists have noticed that this woodland species readily enters buildings, even through very tiny openings.

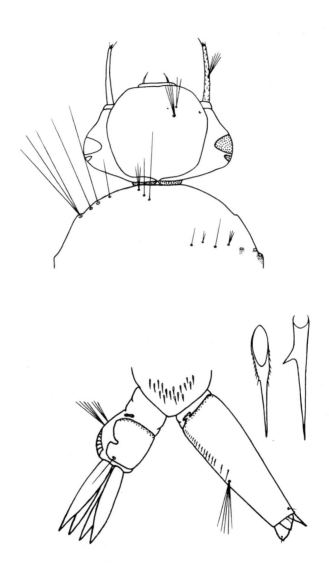

Fig. 46. Larva, *Ae. intrudens*.

117

Aedes melanimon Dyar

> *Aedes melanimon* Dyar, 1924. Ins.Ins.Mens. 12:126
> (Greek: *melan* = black, *heima* = garment, i.e. black-clad. Dyar
> compared its unicolourous dark wing scales with the contrasting
> dark and light veins of *dorsalis*)

Fig. 22a, katepisternum

A small species with pale basal and apical tarsal bands; wing length
3.8–4.3 mm.

Female—Proboscis and palps black, a cluster of white scales at tip of
palp. Pedicels brown, white-scaled on darker median surface. Scutum
with a brown median stripe and posterior half-stripes, separated from
brown lateral areas by white lines. Postprocoxal and hypostigmal areas
many-scaled. Lower mesepimeral setae 1–5. Pale scales on sides of
thorax and erect forked scales on occiput much broader than those of
closely related species, *campestris* and *dorsalis*. Most abdominal tergites
predominantly dark with white T-shaped markings. Sternites mainly
white-scaled. Tarsomeres with indistinct basal and apical white bands.
Fore tarsal claws almost identical to those of *campestris* (Fig. 23a)
(unlike those of *dorsalis*). Wings predominantly dark-scaled. Vein A
dark-scaled (unlike *campestris* and most specimens of *dorsalis*) and
anterior edge of C mainly dark. Richards (1956) noted that the male
genitalia of the three species are distinct. He thought that many specimens previously identified as *dorsalis,* including some infected with
WEE, were probably *melanimon*.

Larva (Fig. 47)—Head setae 5 and 6-C unbranched in most specimens.
15–30 ovoid comb scales in a triangular patch, their apical spines longer
than those of *dorsalis*. Siphon broad, $2\frac{1}{2}$–3×1, pecten even, reaching
mid siphon. 1-S many-branched, inserted just beyond pecten. Papillae
variable, short and bud-like in some specimens. Wood *et al.* (1979)
describe circular and crescent-shaped pigmented spots on the head and
use them to separate *melanimon* from *sticticus* larvae. This character is
not unique, however, because there are identical spots on heads of
dorsalis larvae from the interior of the Province, and a few other aedines
have similar patterns.

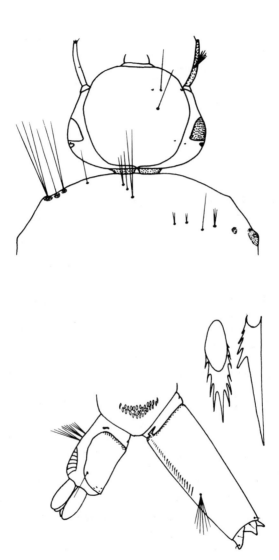

Fig. 47.   Larva, *Ae. melanimon.*

Although *melanimon* is sometimes found in the same habitat as *dorsalis* it generally selects less saline water. It is commonly encountered in irrigation seepage, roadside ditches and sloughs. It has been collected in several localities in the southern dry interior. Bohart & Washino (1978) consider *melanimon* to be an important vector of WEE virus in California.

Aedes mercurator Dyar

Aedes mercurator Dyar, 1920. Ins.Ins.Mens. 8:13
Aedes stimulans albertae Dyar, 1920.
(possibly named after Mercury, the swift messenger of the Greek Gods. Dyar described groups of males flying rapidly from one place to another)

A large species with pale basal bands on the tarsi; wing length 5.5–6 mm.

Female—Proboscis dark-scaled. Palps with scattered pale scales, denser at bases of segments 3 and 4. Pedicels mainly pale-scaled. Scutum with a dark brown median stripe, and yellow sublateral areas (both darker than in *fitchii*) and, in some specimens, narrow posterior half-stripes. Lower mesepimeral setae 1–4. Postprocoxal area sparsely scaled, hypostigmal area bare. Hind tarsomeres with distinct pale basal bands, indistinct on some segments of fore and mid tarsi. Wings dark-scaled, a few pale scales may be found at bases of anterior veins in occasional specimens.

Larva (Fig. 48)—Head setae variable, usually 5-C 4 or 5-branched, 6-C 2 or 3-branched. Seta 1-M barely longer than 5-C (unlike *aboriginis*). About 30 long-spined comb scales in a triangular patch. Siphon about $3\frac{1}{2} \times 1$, pecten even, not reaching mid length. 1-S long, many-branched, inserted just beyond mid siphon. Saddle reaching about $\frac{2}{3}$ around anal segment. Papillae as long as or longer than saddle.

This species was often called *stimulans* until 1977 when it was characterized by Wood. He examined specimens from western Canada, which had been identified as *stimulans* and concluded that most were, in fact, *mercurator*. It appears to be most common in parkland and dry forest but has been found at scattered localities in the Province, although

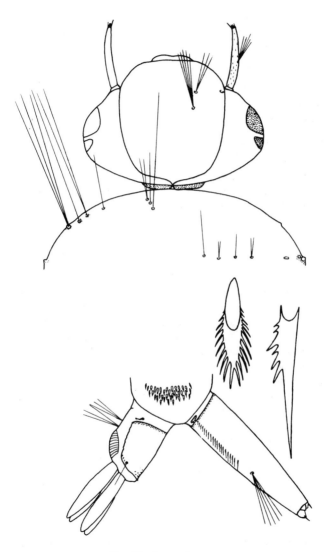

Fig. 48.   Larva, *Ae. mercurator.*

nowhere in great numbers. I have not collected it. The description of the adult is based on material from the Chilcotin; that of the larva on material from the Yukon and Alberta.

Aedes nevadensis Chapman & Barr

Aedes communis nevadensis Chapman & Barr, 1964. Mosq.News 24:439
(Latin: of Nevada)

A medium-sized species with dark unbanded tarsi; wing length 4.5–5 mm. Fig. 34, comb scale.

Female—Indistinguishable from *Ae. communis,* unless reared. In *Ae. nevadensis* the fore claws are narrower and more curved and have longer, narrower lateral teeth than those of *communis* from northern British Columbia.

Larva—The relatively long apical spine of the comb scales on segment AVIII distinguishes this species from *Ae. communis* (Fig. 34).

Larvae were collected in open and thinly shaded pools in the subalpine zone, near Castlegar. Chapman and Barr (1964) believe that habitat distinguishes *Ae. nevadensis* and *communis* and that the latter is found only in woodland pools. Adults of the two species appear to have similar biting habits. I have yet to see confirmed *Ae. communis* larvae from anywhere between Fort Nelson in the north and California in the south, although *nevadensis* occurs from our southern border through Washington and Oregon to Utah and Nevada. More larval collections are needed to clarify the distribution of these two species and to investigate variability in several characters used in their classification.

Aedes nigripes (Zetterstedt)

Culex nigripes Zetterstedt, 1840. Ins.Lapp. 807
(Latin: black feet; i.e. dark tarsi)

Fig. 25b, claw

A medium-sized dark "hairy" species, with unbanded tarsi; wing length 4–5 mm.

Female—Proboscis dark-scaled. Palps dark, with scattered pale scales in some specimens. Pedicels black, with numerous pale and dark scales.

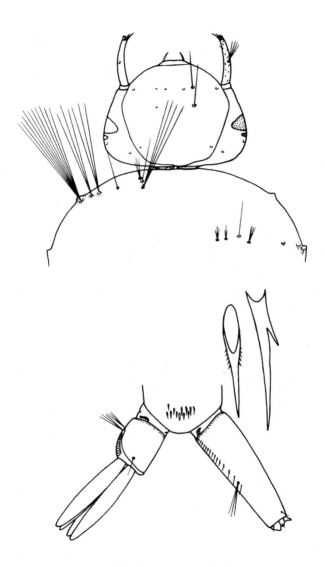

Fig. 49.   Larva, *Ae. nigripes*.

Scutum covered with golden brown scales, becoming paler at margins. The many long dark setae on occiput, scutum and postpronotum give this mosquito a hairy appearance like that of *impiger*. Postprocoxal scale patch present, hypostigmal area bare. Lower mesepimeral setae numerous. Abdominal tergites with broad white basal bands. Tarsi dark with a few pale scales on segment 1. Hind tarsal claw unlike that of *impiger* (Fig. 25a and b). Wings dark scaled, a white patch at bases of veins C and R.

Larva (Fig. 49)—Head setae 5 and 6-C unbranched. 12–18 thorn-shaped comb scales in a ragged double row. Siphon 3×1, pecten reaching mid-siphon or beyond, 1 or more distal teeth widely spaced. 1-S inserted within pecten in most specimens. Saddle completely surrounding anal segment (saddle incomplete in *impiger*). Papillae long.

Along with *impiger,* this is one of the commonest mosquito pests of the high Arctic. Danks & Corbet (1973) give keys to separate all stages of these species. In British Columbia it has been found rarely in the north. It is a strong flyer, probably migratory (Twinn *et al*. 1948) and bites fiercely and persistently. The description is based on material from the North West Territories.

Aedes pionips Dyar

Aedes pionips Dyar, 1919. Ins.Ins.Mens. 7:19
(Greek: *pion* = fat, *ips* = worm, referring to size of larvae which are always larger than *communis* larvae associated with them)

Fig. 26b, katepisternum

A medium-sized species with dark unbanded tarsi; wing length 4.5–5 mm.

Female—Proboscis and palps dark-scaled. Pedicels dark, dorsomedian surface pale-scaled. Scutum clothed with yellow to creamy scales, median paired stripes of brown scales separated by a fine yellow-scaled line and flanked by posterior half-stripes. Postprocoxal scale patch present (absent in *communis*), hypostigmal patch absent. Lower mesepimeral setae 1–4, lacking in occasional specimens. Abdominal tergites with narrow white basal bands. Wings dark-scaled, a small patch of white at base of C in some specimens.

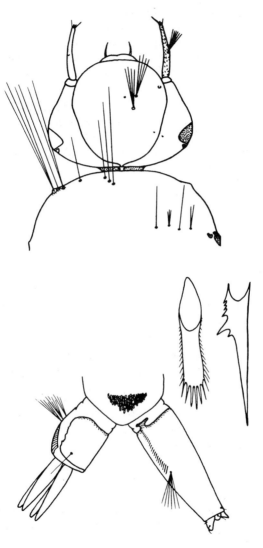

Fig. 50.   Larva, *Ae. pionips*.

Larva (Fig. 50)—Antennae slender, spiculate. Head seta 5-C 4 to 6-branched, 6-C 3 to 5-branched in most specimens (5 and 6-C unbranched in *communis*). 60 or more slipper-shaped comb scales in a patch. Siphon 2½–3 × 1, pecten closely spaced on basal third, 1-S many-branched, inserted about mid siphon. Saddle reaching ⅔ around anal segment. Papillae longer than saddle.

This is a very common mosquito of the northern forests, where it is closely associated with *communis*. The larvae breed in snow melt and rain pools and swamps, but develop more slowly than *communis,* emerging an average of two weeks later, under similar conditions. Extending south along the Rocky Mountains to Colorado, *pionips* has been found in mountainous areas of the interior but most records are from our northern forests. It is not an important pest in British Columbia.

Aedes provocans (Walker)

Culex provocans Walker, 1848. List Dipt.Brit. Mus. 1:17
Culex trichurus Dyar, 1904.
(Latin: provoking, probably referring to its biting habit)

A medium-sized species with dark unbanded tarsi; wing length 4.4–4.8 mm. Siphon of larva with numerous additional multi-branched setae.

Female—Proboscis and palps dark-scaled. Pedicels brown laterally, median surface darker, with pale scales. Scutum greyish white, the broad brown median stripe becoming wider posteriorly. Hypostigmal and postprocoxal scale patches present. Lower mesepimeral setae 3–6. Abdominal tergites with white basal bands, widening laterally. Tibiae and basal tarsomeres dark, with scattered pale scales. Wings brown-scaled, a small patch of white at base of C.

Larva (Fig. 51)—Head seta 5-C 2 or 3-branched, 6-C unbranched. 12–18 thorn-shaped comb scales in a ragged double row. Siphon about 3 × 1, pecten extending to apical ¼, distal 4 or 5 teeth widely spaced. 1-S large, inserted within pecten. Unique among North American aedines is the series of multi-branched setae on lateral and dorsal sufaces of siphon. Saddle almost completely surrounds anal segment. Papillae long and pointed.

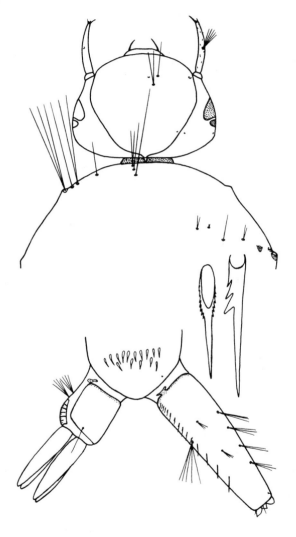

Fig. 51. Larva, *Ae. provocans*.

This is mainly a woodland snowpool species, sometimes found breeding in large open flooded areas, and one of the earliest mosquitoes to emerge in spring (Twinn 1949). In Ontario I have seen diffuse swarms of males circulating in figure of eight patterns at the edge of woods (James *et al*. 1969). It has been found at scattered locations in the eastern half of the Province. Dyar (1904) described the synonym, *trichurus,* from larvae found at Kaslo. It is doubtful if it occurs in sufficient numbers anywhere in the Province to be a nuisance, although the females bite avidly.

Aedes pullatus (Coquillett)

> *Culex pullatus* Coquillett, 1904. Proc.Ent.Soc.Wash. 6:168
> (Latin: clad in black; referring to its overall colour)

A dark, small to medium mosquito with unbanded tarsi; wing length 3.5–4.9 mm.

Female—Proboscis black. Palps black with scattered pale scales basally. Pedicels dark, pale-scaled medially. Scutum with yellowish-brown scales, paler towards margins; a narrow bare median line is bordered by two stripes of sparse darker brown scales and in some specimens, a pair of dark brown half-stripes curve posteriorly. Hypostigmal area with a conspicuous patch of white scales, postprocoxal area bare. Lower mesepimeral setae 1–5. Abdominal tergites with basal white bands. Tarsi dark, tarsomere 1 with scattered white scales. Wings dark-scaled, a patch of pale scales at base of C.

Larva (Fig. 52)—Head seta 5-C 5 to 7-branched, 6-C 2 to 5-branched. 30–60 long, variously shaped comb scales in a triangular patch. Siphon about 3×1, pecten evenly spaced on basal third. 1-S large, inserted before mid siphon. Saddle reaching about ⅔ around anal segment. Papillae long and pointed.

This woodland species has been found in our northern regions and on and around mountains further south in the Province. Coquillett described it from specimens found at Kaslo. It develops in snow melt and alpine meadow pools and, at lower elevations, in the flooded margins of streams, frequently those bordering woodland. It emerges later in the season than most other species. The females may be encountered at any time of day in the woods and attack freely. It is not sufficiently numerous to be considered a pest in British Columbia.

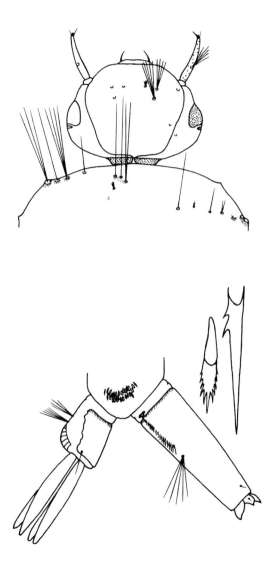

Fig. 52. Larva, *Ae. pullatus*.

Aedes punctor (Kirby)

Culex punctor Kirby, 1837. Richardson's Fauna Bor.-Amer. 4:309
(Latin: probably an agent noun, meaning one who makes
punctures)

A medium-sized species with dark unbanded tarsi; wing length
4.0–4.7 mm.

Female—Proboscis and palps dark-scaled. Pedicels vary from yellow to
black, usually darker medially. Scutum with yellow scales laterally, a
broad dark brown median stripe or paired stripes and posterolateral half-
stripes. Postprocoxal scale patch present, hypostigmal area bare. Probasisternum bare or, if not, with fewer scales than *hexodontus*. Lower
mesepimeral setae 1–5. Abdominal tergites with white basal bands.
Wing scales dark, a few white scales at the base of C in some specimens.
The adults are very similar to those of *aboriginis* and *hexodontus*.

Larva (Fig. 53)—Head setae 5 and 6-C 1 or 2-branched. 9–20 thorn-
shaped comb scales in a straggling row (smaller and usually more
numerous than those of *hexodontus*, *see* p. 108). Siphon 3×1, pecten
teeth evenly spaced, 1-S many-branched inserted at about mid length.
Saddle surrounding anal segment (saddle incomplete in *aboriginis*).
Papillae long, tapered.

This is one of the dark-legged aedines that has proved difficult to pin
down in the past, and it is possible that a number of Provincial records of
punctor may actually refer to *hexodontus*. *Punctor* is a snowpool mosquito and one of the earliest to develop in the spring. It is found across the
Province, mainly in the mountains and forests where it can be abundant.
On one occasion a swarm of male *punctor* (mixed with other species)
formed a dark cloud extending as far as the eye could see over a railway
track in Manitoba (Hocking *et al.* 1950). In Ontario, I frequently observed compact swarms of *punctor* over contrasting elevated markers
(James *et al.* 1969). Another vicious persistent biter, it is a serious pest of
man and animals in wooded areas.

If the breeding sites can be found the larvae can be controlled with
little or no environmental damage because the snow melt pools dry up in
the summer and harbour few other insects.

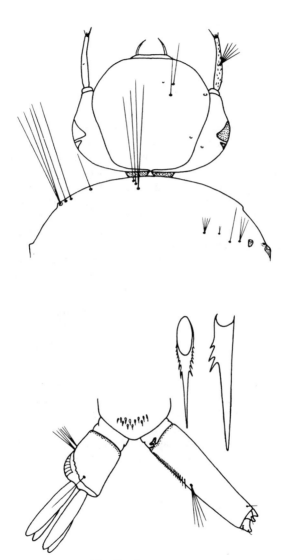

Fig. 53.   Larva, *Ae. punctor.*

Aedes riparius Dyar & Knab

Aedes riparius Dyar & Knab, 1907. J.N.Y.Ent.Soc. 15:213
(Latin: frequenting river banks, described from specimens found
along the banks of the Assiniboine River)

A medium to large mosquito with pale basal bands on the tarsi; wing
length 4.5–5.3 mm.

Female—Proboscis dark, pale-scaled at mid length. Palps black, with
pale scales apically on each segment. Pedicels brownish, median surface
dark-scaled with a few pale scales in some specimens. Median area of
scutum covered with orange-brown scales, becoming paler at margins.
Postprocoxal area with few to many scales. Hypostigmal area scaled in
most specimens. No lower mesepimeral setae. Most abdominal tergites
brown-scaled with indistinct pale basal bands and with few to many white
scales in dark areas, tergites VI and VII mainly white. Tarsomeres with
white basal bands, broadest on hind legs. Wings mainly dark-scaled,
some white intermixed. The females are very similar to those of *aloponotum* but fortunately, their distribution does not overlap in the
Province and the male genitalia are distinct.

Larva (Fig. 54)—Head setae 5 & 6-C long, 2 or 3-branched. 6–8 large
dark thorn-shaped comb scales in a regular row. Siphon 3½ × 1, pecten
teeth closely spaced on basal third, then 2 or 3 teeth widely spaced,
almost to mid siphon. Saddle reaching ¾ or more around anal segment.
Ventral margin of saddle notched.

Ae. riparius inhabits open parkland where tree-shaded pools are
available. It has been found in the Cariboo, in Peace River country and
adjacent boreal forest. In Ontario, males swarmed in compact groups
over willow branches and small bushes (James *et al.* 1969). The females
are reported to bite by night or day but although the species is found from
coast to coast, it is only common in true prairie habitats.

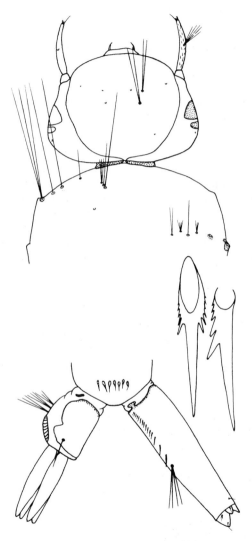

Fig. 54.   Larva, *Ae. riparius*.

Aedes sierrensis (Ludlow)

Taeniorhynchus sierrensis Ludlow, 1905. Can.Ent. 37:231
Aedes varipalpus, of authors, not Coquillett
(Latin: of the Sierras, described from specimens found in the Sierra
Nevada Mtns., California)

A small to medium-sized mosquito, breeding in tree-holes, its tarsal
segments with characteristic silvery white bands; wing length 2.9–4.8
mm.

Female—Proboscis dark-scaled. Palps dark, apices of segments white-
scaled, distal segment entirely white in some specimens. Pedicels dark,
dorsomedian surface white-scaled. Scutum with a median stripe and
curved lateral lines of golden scales on a background of curved dark
brown scales. No lower mesepimeral setae or postprocoxal or hypostigmal scale patches. Abdominal tergites dark with strongly contrasting
white basal bands, widest at centre, narrowing laterally. Hind tarsomeres
1 & 4 with broad silvery white basal and apical bands, 2 & 3 with broad
basal and narrow apical bands, 5 entirely white. Wings dark, a patch of
white scales at base of C.

Larva (Fig. 55)—Antennae smooth, 1-A unbranched (as in *hendersoni*).
Head setae 5 & 6-C 1 or 2-branched. 12–23 long comb scales in a patch.
Siphon about 3×1, pecten evenly spaced on basal ¼ to ⅓. 1-S many
branched, inserted before mid siphon. Saddle small, reaching about half
way around anal segment. 1-X long, 2-branched. Papillae long broad and
bluntly rounded, and swimming setae sparse (as in *hendersoni*).

This species was known as *varipalpus* until 1957 (Belkin & Mac-
Donald). Like *hendersoni*, it breeds in tree-holes but *sierrensis* is also
occasionally found in artificial containers. Eggs laid in late summer are
reported to hatch in the fall and winter is spent in the larval stage. I have
found that eggs laid in captivity in the Lower Mainland will hatch when
immersed in early December and evidently do not have a rigid diapause.
Fourth instar larvae, however, will not pupate until the days reach a
critical length in the following spring (Arnell & Nielsen 1972). *Sierrensis*
breeds in holes in a variety of deciduous trees across the south of the
Province and, in the Kootenays, was once discovered 500 m above the
treeline in an artificial container (Dyar 1904). The most northerly record

134

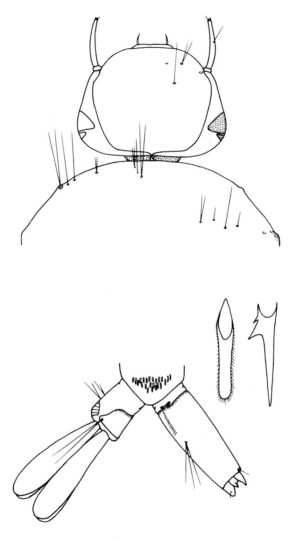

Fig. 55.   Larva, *Ae. sierrensis*.

is from Terrace (Arnell & Nielsen 1972). Males have the habit of dodging around warm-blooded animals, where they seize and mate with females that approach to take blood. Biting females enter houses in the Lower Mainland between May and August. Adults vary greatly in size. They tend to be small when temperatures are high, but their size is probably also influenced by the nutrient content of the water in the breeding site. The smallest females can penetrate normal insect screening (7/cm mesh).

Control of larvae in the breeding sites is usually impractical, although rot cavities in garden and boulevard trees should be plugged when found. Fine window screening is probably the best solution in wooded areas. The release of sterile males or biological control techniques using parasites or predators would be worth investigating if the species becomes an important pest. It transmits Dog heartworm (*Dirofilaria immitis*) in many parts of its range.

Aedes spencerii (Theobald)

Culex spencerii Theobald, 1901. Mon.Culic. 2:99
(named after W. I. Spencer who first collected it in Manitoba)

A small to medium-sized pale species with grey wings and unbanded tarsi; wing length 3.5–4 mm.

Female—Proboscis dark-scaled. Palps white-speckled apically. Pedicels with many pale scales on dorsomedian surface. Scutum greyish, the broad median stripe brown-scaled, sometimes divided longitudinally by a narrow grey stripe, sometimes bordered by dark posterior half-stripes; lateral margins and prescutellar space whitish-scaled. Mesepimeron covered with scales almost to lower margin. Postprocoxal and hypostigmal scale patches present, lower mesepimeral setae absent. Abdominal pattern variable, tergites either with white basal bands, sometimes with a central white stripe, or almost completely white-scaled. Tarsi unbanded but with pale scales on posterior surfaces. Wing veins appearing alternately dark and pale-scaled.

Larva (Fig. 56)—Head setae 5 & 6-C unbranched, in rare specimens one of them may be 2-branched. Thorax and abdomen spiculate (200×). 7–25 thorn-shaped comb scales in a ragged double row. Siphon short and stout, 2–3 × 1, pecten reaching mid siphon or just beyond, distal 2 or 3

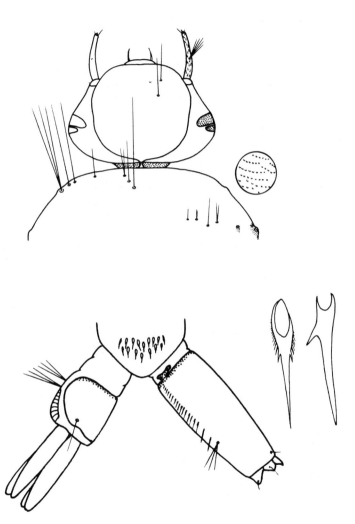

Fig. 56.   Larva, *Ae. spencerii*.

teeth widely spaced. 1-S short, 2 to 4-branched, inserted just beyond pecten. Saddle reaching more than ⅘ around anal segment. 1-X short, unbranched.

Ae. spencerii has two distinct forms in British Columbia considered by some to be separate species. (Further south, the forms merge, becoming indistinguishable.) The *spencerii* form (abdominal tergites almost completely white) is the typical, and almost the dominant, species of prairie grasslands. Its only capture within our borders, apart from a dubious record from Kaslo, was made in the Peace River country, east of the Rocky Mountains. The *idahoensis* form (abdominal tergites distinctly banded) inhabits wooded and mountainous country in southern British Columbia and in Montana, Idaho and eastern Washington. It was first collected in Canada near Oliver by Hearle (1923b) who correctly predicted that it would be found further north in the Okanagan. It has been found there in the same pools as *vexans* and *dorsalis*, in Kamloops along with *vexans* and in various other localites.

The larvae breed in many different habitats, including snow and rain pools, irrigation seepage and floodwater. It may produce more than one brood per season. Knab (1907) described the females as voracious blood suckers in early summer, making life on the prairies a torture for man and beast. Later in the season, however, he found both females and males feeding on nectar from willow catkins. Fortunately it is not very common anywhere in the Province. One specimen from Saskatchewan was found naturally infected with WEE virus (McLintock *et al.* 1970).

Aedes sticticus (Meigen)

> *Culex sticticus* Meigen, 1838. Syst.Beschr.Zweifl.Ins. 7:1
> *Culex hirsuteron* Theobald, 1901
> *Culex aestivalis* Dyar, 1904
> *Aedes aldrichi* Dyar & Knab, 1908
> *Aedes lateralis,* of authors, not Meigen
> (Greek: punctured or stung)

A small greyish mosquito with unbanded tarsi; wing length 3.2–4 mm.

Female—Proboscis and palps dark-scaled. Pedicels yellow laterally, darker medially and pale-scaled. Scutum with paired golden brown

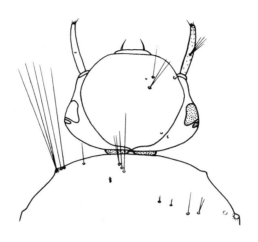

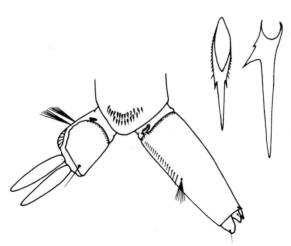

Fig. 57. Larva, *Ae. sticticus*.

median stripes and posterolateral half-stripes on a background of pale yellowish-grey scales. No postprocoxal or hypostigmal scale patches or lower mesepimeral setae. Abdominal tergites with narrow white basal bands, broadening laterally. Legs mainly dark, a few pale scales among the black. Wing scales dark, a white patch at base of C in some specimens.

Larva (Fig. 57)—Head seta 5-C 2 to 4-branched and 6-C 1 to 3-branched. 20–25 thorn-shaped comb scales in a triangular patch. Siphon short and stout, $2\frac{1}{2}$–3 × 1; pecten teeth closely spaced on basal third, then widening to just beyond middle. 1-S inserted beyond pecten, shorter than apical diameter of siphon. Saddle reaching $\frac{4}{5}$ or more around anal segment.

For many years, variations in the pattern of scales on the scutum lead to *sticticus* being regarded as two separate species, *aldrichi* in the lower Fraser and North Thompson valleys and *hirsuteron,* further east in the lower interior valleys (Hearle 1932). The synonym, *aestivalis,* was described from larvae found in the Kootenays. In years of widespread flooding, *sticticus* used to be one of the commonest species across the south of the Province and, with *vexans,* the dominant mosquito pest in the lower Fraser Valley (Hearle 1926). In the last five years, however, the Fraser has not flooded significantly and *sticticus* has been scarce in the valley. Swarms of about 50 males form in early evening 1 m or so above the ground, often in willow growth (Hearle 1920). Most commonly, the larvae develop in wooded river flats along with *vexans* and *cinereus,* but are seldom found in open flood water where *vexans* can breed in enormous numbers. Hatching occurs immediately after the eggs are flooded, generally in late May or early June. If, as is often the case, the river has several peaks at intervals of a week or so, each peak will produce a fresh hatch of larvae. The eggs remain viable for at least five years (Gibson 1933) so that one or two seasons can pass when the species does not appear, thus complicating control measures. Adults readily invade houses and most are small enough to penetrate 12-mesh screening (Hearle 1920). They have a flight range of several miles, and females bite viciously by day or night.

Aerial photographs of flooded areas, along with surveys of the larvae there provide a sound basis for control of this pest using selective methods.

Aedes togoi (Theobald)

Culiselsa togoi Theobald, 1907. Mon.Culic. 4:379
(presumably named after its Japanese collector, Togo)

A large, elegantly marked mosquito with distinctively banded tarsi; wing length 5 mm. It is restricted to rocky coastal areas.

Female—Proboscis uniformly dark. Palps dark, tipped with silver scales. Pedicels silver scaled on dorsomedian surface. Scutum predominantly brown to the naked eye, with six longitudinal stripes of golden scales, broadening anteriorly; curve of outermost stripes following suture, to scutal angle. Prescutellar space bordered by golden brown scales. Postprocoxal and hypostigmal areas bare. 4 lower mesepimeral setae. Abdominal tergites with dark brown scales and silvery white basal bands widening laterally. Dark scales of abdomen and legs with blue-green iridescence. Upper surfaces of femora and tibiae dark, pale scales below. Tarsomeres with white basal and apical bands, basal bands lacking on segment 5 in some specimens. Wings dark-scaled, a few pale scales at base of C.

Larva (Fig. 58)—Head setae 5 and 6-C close to anterior margin of head, 6 or more-branched. Comb scales slipper-shaped, small and very numerous (50–100 or more) in a semicircular patch. Siphon short, 2–$2\frac{1}{2} \times 1$, pecten teeth even, extending beyond middle. 1-S large many-branched, inserted beyond pecten. Saddle small, 1-X long unbranched, not inserted on saddle. Papillae very short, almost hemispherical.

In North America, this species was first collected from Cordova Bay, Vancouver Island, by Dr. R. Ring of the University of Victoria, and shown at the meeting of the Canadian Entomological Society there in 1971. An adult specimen in the Canadian National Collection, however, appears to have been collected 20 years earlier at Horseshoe Bay by C. D. Garrett. Dr. M. Trimble and I have found it on the Gulf Islands, all along the Sechelt Peninsula and on Howe Sound, 46 km north of Horseshoe Bay. This species may have been introduced from Japan as Wood *et al.* (1979) suggest, but when milder climates prevailed, it could have been widely distributed around the Pacific rim. If its range is found to extend further north, I would find it difficult to believe that it is a recently introduced species. The larvae are found in rock pools just above high

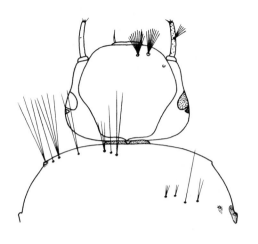

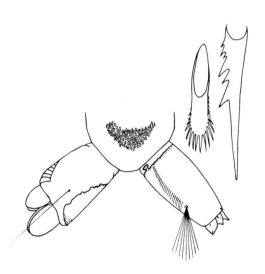

Fig. 58.   Larva, *Ae. togoi.*

143

tide. They can easily be overlooked as they are able to remain for long periods in the debris at the bottom of the pools without surfacing. Adults bite humans readily but do not fly far from shore. *Ae. togoi* can transmit several diseases including Japanese B encephalitis and filariasis in Malaya, Japan and the coastal area of U.S.S.R. north of the Sea of Japan (La Casse & Yamaguti 1950). Fortunately these diseases do not occur in British Columbia.

Aedes vexans (Meigen)

> *Culex vexans* Meigen, 1830, Syst.Beschr.Zweifl. Ins. 6:241
> *Culex sylvestris* Theobald, 1901
> (Latin: annoying)

Fig. 19d, tarsus

A small to medium-sized species with unusually narrow white basal bands on the tarsomeres and indented bands on the abdominal tergites; wing length 3.5–4 mm.

Female—Proboscis dark-scaled. Palps dark with pale scales at both ends of segment 4. Pedicels brown, a few pale scales medially. Scutum clad in golden brown scales, paler near margins. No postprocoxal or hypostigmal scale patches or lower mesepimeral setae. Abdominal tergites with white basal bands, distinctively indented at the middle and narrowed laterally. Narrow white basal bands on all hind and some fore and mid tarsomeres. Wing scales dark, a few pale scales at bases of veins.

Larva (Fig. 59)—Head seta 5-C 2 to 4-branched, 6-C 2 to 3-branched. 9–12 dark thorn-shaped comb scales in an irregular row. Siphon $3\frac{1}{2} \times 1$, pecten reaching mid length, 2 or 3 distal teeth long and widely spaced. 1-S shorter than diameter of apex of siphon, inserted beyond pecten. Saddle nearly surrounding anal segment. Seta 1-X 1 or 2-branched.

Ae. vexans is one of the most widely distributed species in Canada. Horsfall *et al.* (1973) wrote "Across its range it is the principal cause for daytime annoyance from mosquitoes outdoors, especially in suburban areas. It has been the reason for the establishment of abatement districts in metropolitan areas across central USA-48 and southern Canada." It is probably the worst pest mosquito in southern British Columbia, feeding on man and domestic animals (Hearle 1926). It can be found both in the

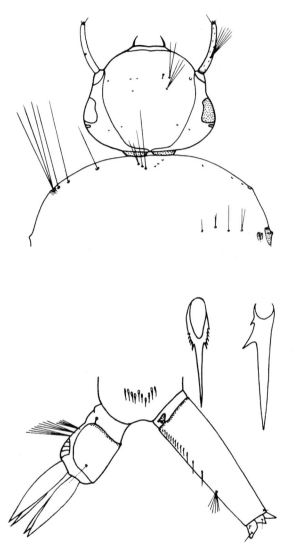

Fig. 59.   Larva, *Ae. vexans*.

open and in woodland, from sea level to alpine regions, and breeds in flood water, irrigation run-off and woodland pools. In the lower Fraser Valley both males and females have been seen feeding on white *Spiraea* and males swarming in considerable numbers at dusk. Hearle wrote in 1926 of the "incalculable numbers" produced when Sumas prairie flooded. Egg-hatching is temperature dependent (Brust & Costello 1969) and as flooding or rainfall may immerse the eggs several times in any one season, each initiating a further hatch, the problem requires close vigilance by control workers. In addition, adults have a long flight range, estimated at 20–50 km by several writers. Horsfall *et al.* (1973) believe that *vexans* can travel for hundreds of km in the low jet stream. These facts make control measures extremely difficult. The species has been found naturally infected by WEE virus in Alberta (Morgante & Shemanchuk 1975), Saskatchewan (McLintock *et al.* 1970) and in the north western U.S. (Gjullin & Eddy 1972).

Ditching and dyking have undoubtedly reduced the numbers of *Ae. vexans* in the lower Fraser Valley since the 1920's and, in Coquitlam, *vexans* is still controlled by altering water levels in marshy areas.

Genus *Culex*

Culex Linnaeus, 1758, Syst.Nat.Ed., 10:602

Linnaeus used *culex,* the Latin word for mosquito when he described the common house mosquito, *Culex pipiens.* All mosquitoes described in the following 50 years were placed in this genus. In 1818 Meigen decided that there were at least two other major types of mosquito, which he therefore renamed and placed in the genera *Anopheles* and *Aedes.* Only three *Culex* species, one of which is *pipiens,* are known to occur in British Columbia.

The pale cuticle gives the adults an overall brown colour. The females can readily be separated from those of *Anopheles* by the short palps and trilobed scutellum, from those of *Aedes* by the blunt abdomen and from *Culiseta* and *Mansonia* females by the absence of both pre- and postspiracular setae.

Eggs are laid in rafts on the surface of almost any standing water.

Larvae have a long narrow respiratory siphon with a short pecten at the base composed of rather small teeth. The siphon lacks basal seta 1-S, but four or more pairs of branched setae arise ventrally beyond the pecten.

146

Pupae should be kept alive and allowed to emerge.

All our species overwinter as fertilized females and can produce several generations a year.

Genus *Culex*

Key to adult females in British Columbia

1.   Tarsal segments with pale basal bands; proboscis with band of pale scales at mid length.. 2

        Tarsi and proboscis without pale bands................................ 3

2. (1) Femora and tibiae with a line of pale scales on lateral surface (Fig. 60); median surface of pedicel with pale scales .... *tarsalis* (p. 152)

        Femora and tibiae unlined; pedicels uniformly dark-scaled .... *peus**

3. (1) Abdominal tergites with pale basal bands. Medium sized domestic species.. *pipiens* (p. 148)

        Tergites with pale apical bands. Small species seldom near houses.. *territans* (p. 154)

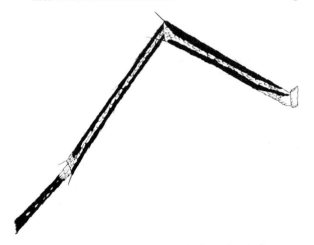

Fig. 60.   Femur and tibia, *Cx. tarsalis* (posterior view).

---

* Not yet found in British Columbia.

Genus *Culex*

Key to fourth instar larvae in British Columbia

1. Head setae 5 & 6-C long and 1 or 2-branched; siphon very long and slender, 6×1 .... *territans* (p. 154)

   Setae 5 & 6-C more than 4-branched, shorter than head; siphon shorter, about 4×1 2

2. (1) Siphon with 5 pairs of aligned setae; tip of antenna pigmented beyond seta 1-A .... *tarsalis* (p. 152)

   4 or 5 pairs of siphon setae, penultimate pair out of line; tip of antenna pigmented, or not............................. 3

3. (2) Tip of antenna not pigmented; 4 pairs of siphon setae; apex of saddle without prominent pigmented spicules .... *pipiens* (p. 148)

   Tip of antenna pigmented; 5 pairs of siphon setae; apex of saddle with prominent dark spicules........................ *peus**

Culex pipiens L.

Culex pipiens Linnaeus, 1758, Syst.Nat.10th Ed.:602
(Latin: piping, referring to the whine of its flight)

A small to medium-sized, dull brown mosquito with unbanded tarsi; wing length 3.5–4 mm. It is appropriately called the common house mosquito.

Female—Proboscis and palps dark. Pedicels uniformly dark brown. Scutum covered with golden brown scales. Abdominal tergites black with pale basal bands, widest at the centre, narrowing laterally before joining lateral triangular pale patches. Tarsi brown. Wings dark-scaled.

Larva (Fig. 61)—Antennae long, spiculate, apical third constricted beyond 1-A. Head setae 5 and 6-C 4 or more branched. More than 35 slipper-shaped comb scales in a triangular patch. Siphon $4–5 \times 1$, pecten on basal quarter. 4 many-branched setae inserted beyond pecten, penultimate one slightly out of line, placed more dorsally. Saddle surrounding anal segment.

---

* Not yet found in British Columbia.

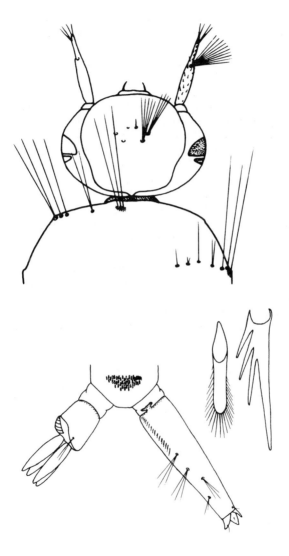

Fig. 61.   Larva, *Cx. pipiens*.

It is hard to believe that *pipiens* was once rare in the province. Hearle wrote in 1926 "It would appear that this species has been introduced comparatively recently". It "has been taken, but is very rare, and so far has been found at one point only" (Vancouver). In recent years, it has spread widely and increased enormously in numbers and is now common from Vancouver Island at least to the Okanagan.

On emergence from hibernation fertilized females seek a blood meal and soon lay their eggs in boat-shaped rafts on the surface of water in sewage lagoons, drainage ditches, catch basins, paddling pools, tin cans and also in natural open pools and swamps. The new generation matures, mates and lays its eggs in three to five weeks. Several generations are produced each season, the number depending on the temperature of the breeding site. In the Lower Mainland I have seen groups of about ten males swarming over Douglas Spirea bushes in summer and close to the south walls of buildings later in the season, often until the first killing frost. By then the mated females have found humid places to hibernate, often within buildings.

There has been much debate about the varied behaviour of this species and whether or not there are two strains, only one of which bites humans. In the many ditches of the Richmond area it is often abundant, yet seldom annoying outdoors. On the other hand, it is a pest when it enters houses in late summer and bites the inhabitants. Most residents in the southwest of the Province have experienced its whine around their heads as they tried to sleep. Although the Richmond strain seldom bites outdoors it has been successfully colonized and will feed on guinea pigs in a warm humid laboratory (Gillespie 1978). Specimens naturally infected with SLE and WEE have been found in Washington State (Gjullin & Eddy 1972).

Culex tarsalis Coquillett

Culex tarsalis Coquillett, 1896, Can.Ent. 28:43
(Greek: having to do with tarsi, referring to their distinctive pale bands)

Fig. 60, femur and tibia

A medium-sized mosquito with banded tarsi and a broad crisp white band on the proboscis; wing length 4–4.4 mm.

Female—Proboscis long and dark with a broad white band near the middle. Palps white-tipped. Pedicels with a patch of white scales on median surface. Scutum covered with narrow brown scales, a fine line of white scales extending forward each side of prescutellar space and terminating in a white spot. Abdominal tergites with scattered pale scales on I, a basal triangular patch on II and white basal bands on III-VII. Wing scales dark, a few pale ones near base of C. Legs brown-scaled, hind femur and tibia with a continuous or interrupted row of white scales laterally. White basal and apical bands on all hind and most fore and mid tarsomeres.

Larva (Fig. 62)—Antennae long, dark at base and apex, pale between and strongly spiculate to insertion of 1-A. Head seta 5-C 4 or more branched, 6-C 3 or more branched. 50 or more slipper-shaped comb scales in a patch (dotted in fig.). Siphon about 5×1, pecten on basal third. 5 many-branched setae inserted in line, beyond pecten. Saddle surrounding anal segment. Papillae longer than saddle.

Cx. tarsalis is common from the coast to the Okanagan and has been taken as far north as Little Fort on the North Thompson and as far east as Cranbrook. It breeds in a variety of water sources such as flooded meadows, open ditches, irrigation seepage, borrow pits and sewage lagoons, and can tolerate a high degree of pollution. Egg rafts are laid in early summer and there are several generations each season. The adults from well fed larvae can mature eggs without a blood meal (Washino & Shad-Del 1969) but normally they take blood from birds, cattle and man, entering houses at night and biting readily. In central Alberta, its preferred hosts are birds, 52%, followed by cattle and man, each 12% (Shemanchuk *et al*. 1963). Females hibernate in crevices of rock slides, rodent burrows, culverts and cellars. *Cx. tarsalis* is the principal vector of WEE

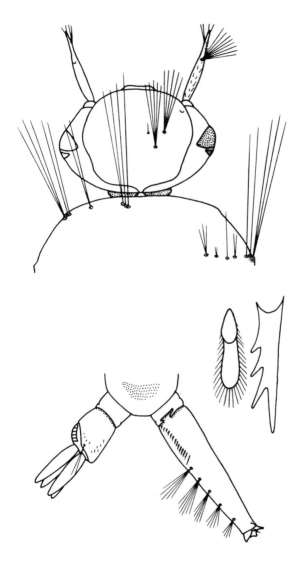

Fig. 62.   Larva, *Cx. tarsalis*.

153

virus in western Canada (Burton & McLintock 1970) and in the northwestern States (Gjullin & Eddy 1972).

In British Columbia, horses are usually immunized annually against WEE but in regions where the virus occurs (Okanagan and Shuswap Lakes) pesticides will probably be used against both larvae and adults when they and the virus are abundant.

Culex territans Walker

> *Culex territans* Walker, 1856, Ins.Saund.Dipt. 1:428
> *Culex saxatilis* Grossbeck, 1905.
> *Culex apicalis,* of authors, not Adams
> *Culex testaceous,* of authors, not van der Wulp
> (Latin: *territo* = frightening)

A very small brown mosquito with dark unbanded tarsi and diagnostic narrow white apical bands on the abdominal tergites; wing length 3–3.3 mm.

Female—Proboscis long, brown-scaled. Palps short, black. Pedicels brown with a few white scales mediodorsally. Scutum with pale brown scales, a pair of indefinite pale spots near centre, and two indistinct lines, bare of scales, either side of the midline. Abdominal tergites with narrow white apical bands widening laterally. Wing scales black.

Larva (Fig. 63)—Antennae as long as head, spiculate to constriction, 1-A large. Head setae 5 and 6-C 1 or 2-branched, 5-C shorter than 6-C. 35 or more comb scales in a patch (dotted in fig.). Siphon very long and slender, 6×1, tapering nearly to tip then slightly flared; pecten on basal third, 5 many-branched setae beyond it, not always in line. Saddle surrounding anal segment, strongly spiculate dorsoapically.

This is another species which has been called several different names in British Columbia—*saxatilis* is a synonym of *territans; apicalis* is now applied to a similar species that occurs in the southwestern States and *testaceous,* now considered a synonym of *Ma. perturbans,* was wrongly used for *territans* in a number of papers by Dyar and Hearle.

The larvae breed in permanent pools and swamps, grassy ditches and borrow pits, but do not develop in polluted water. Females overwinter in mammal burrows and under logs and rock piles. It has been found across the south of the Province, but nowhere in large numbers. It seldom bites man, preferring to take blood from amphibians.

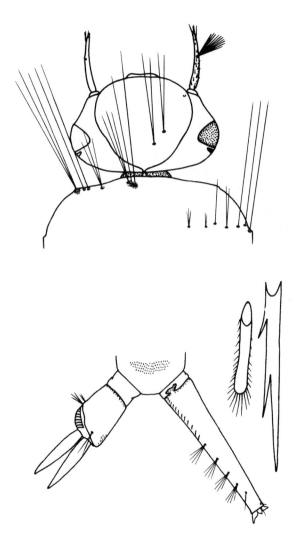

Fig. 63.   Larva, *Cx. territans*.

Genus *Culiseta*

Culiseta Felt, 1904, N.Y. State Mus.Bull.79:391

Culiseta, a feminine diminutive of the masculine *Culex* (ancient Romans did not sex their mosquitoes) was used to separate the species we now know as *impatiens* from the genus *Culex.* The name, *Theobaldia,* was used by several authors until it was found to be invalid having already been used for a genus of Molluscs.

Culiseta females have short palps and a trilobed scutellum and the blunt abdomen resembles that of *Anopheles, Culex* and *Mansonia.* Some of our species have patches of dark scales on the wings similar to those of anophelines. Dubious specimens will have to be examined for the presence of prespiracular and absence of postspircular setae.

The single pair of branched setae (1-S) at the base of the siphon characterizes larvae of this genus.

The pupae are difficult to distinguish with certainty from those of other genera. Most collectors will keep them until the adults emerge.

Most *Culiseta* species in our Province lay their eggs in rafts on water surfaces. *Cs. morsitans,* however, lays egg rafts on vegetation at the margin of its breeding sites. If the eggs are washed down into the water some may hatch and larvae may overwinter in the benthic debris. If not washed down, the eggs probably overwinter and hatch like those of aedines when flooded in the spring. Most *Culiseta* species overwinter as fertilized, and probably blood-fed, females and at least some species can produce several generations each year.

Genus *Culiseta*

Key to adult females in British Columbia

Fig. 64.   Femur, *Cs. particeps*.

Genus *Culiseta*

Key to fourth instar larvae in British Columbia

1.   Siphon short and broad, 3×1 or less; antennae about ½ length of head 2

Siphon long and slender, 5×1 or more; antennae about as long as head 6

2. (1) Head setae 5 & 6-C of equal length and number of branches (mostly 6-branched) .... *impatiens* (p. 160)

Seta 6-C longer and less branched than 5-C 3

3. (2) Saddle seta 1-X robust, about as long as saddle, 2-branched in most specimens .... *inornata* (p. 164)

1-X fine, less than ¾ as long as saddle, 2 to 4-branched 4

---

* Not yet found in British Columbia.

4. (3) Antennae pale, not prominently spiculate; prothoracic
        seta 1-P 3 to 5-branched..............................*incidens* (p. 162)
        Antennae dark with prominent spicules; 1-P unbranched
        or 3 to 5-branched...5
5. (4) Apical margin of saddle smooth dorsally; seta 1-P un-
        branched..*alaskensis* (p. 158)
        Apical margin with coarse spicules dorsally; 1-P 3 to 5-
        branched...*particeps**
6. (1) Head seta 5-C 4 to 5-branched; cratal and precratal setae
        20 or more...*morsitans* (p. 166)
        5-C 7 to 8-branched; 17 or 18 cratal and precratal setae
        ....*minnesotae* (p. 168)

Culiseta alaskaensis (Ludlow)

Theobaldia alaskaensis Ludlow, 1906 Can.Ent. 38:326
(Latin: of Alaska, first specimens sent from there to Ludlow)

A very large mosquito with spotted wings and striking white bands on its tarsal segments; wing length 6–7 mm.

Female—Proboscis and palps dark with scattered white scales. Pedicels brown, yellowish-scaled on darker median surface. Scutum mainly brown-scaled; scattered white scales form ill-defined paired median spots in some specimens. Abdominal tergites dark with broad white basal bands. Tarsomeres with white basal bands, broadest on hind legs. Wings mainly dark-scaled, mixed white and dark on veins C, Sc and R_1 and dark scales clustered to form small spots at bases of R_s, R_{2+3}, R_{4+5} and M_{1+2}. Cross vein r-m dark-scaled.

Larva (Fig. 65)—Antennae short, spiculate. Head seta 5-C 5 to 7-branched and shorter than 6-C which is 3 to 4-branched. 40 or more slipper-shaped comb scales in a patch. Siphon about 3×1, pecten on basal $\frac{1}{5}$ followed by a row of long setae reaching apical $\frac{1}{4}$. 1-S inserted near base of siphon. Saddle surrounding anal segment, 2 or more precratal setae inserted on saddle. 1-X very short and branched. Papillae long and pointed.

---

* Not yet found in British Columbia.

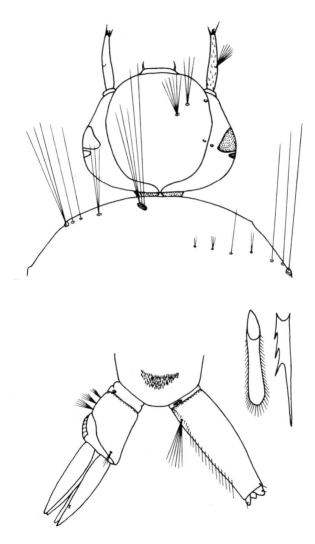

Fig. 65.   Larva, *Cs. alaskaensis*.

This was the largest mosquito Hearle found in his 1926 survey of the Fraser Valley. It is widespread throughout the Province, but is nowhere very numerous. Females spend the winter in sheltered spots, sometimes under bark, and emerge in the spring to seek a blood meal and develop their eggs. These are laid in rafts on the surface of pools or ditches with a good deal of emergent vegetation. Even in the south of the Province there appears to be only one generation a year. The females bite in the shade but are seldom significant pests.

Culiseta impatiens (Walker)

Culex impatiens Walker, 1848, List Dipt.Brit.Mus. 1:5
(Latin: impatient, referring to its attack)

A large to very large, dull brown mosquito, with unbanded tarsi; wing length 5–7 mm.

Female—Proboscis and palps dark with a few scattered white scales. Pedicels brown, a few pale scales on darker median surface in some specimens. Scutum with mingled brown and yellowish scales, a pair of yellowish lines extending posteriorly from paired pale spots. Abdominal tergites dark with narrow white basal bands. Tarsi dark. Wing scales dark, more numerous in elongate darker regions at bases of veins R_s, R_{2+3}, M_{1+2} and in area of crossvein r-m.

Larva (Fig. 66)—Antennae spiculate. Head setae 5 & 6-C 5 or more-branched and almost equal in length (6-C longer than 5-C in *incidens* and *inornata*). 40 or more slipper-shaped comb scales in a patch (dotted in fig.). Siphon 3×1, a short pecten near base followed by a row of setae almost reaching apical ¼. 1-S large, many-branched, inserted basally within pecten. Saddle surrounding anal segment. 1-X branched, shorter than saddle.

This species is found across the Province, most commonly in the Fraser Valley, but nowhere in great numbers. The females emerge from hibernation in early spring, occasionally on warm days when there is still snow on the ground. They oviposit in shaded pools. They are not aggressive biters, and while they attack man on occasion, they usually take blood from other mammals, chiefly cattle.

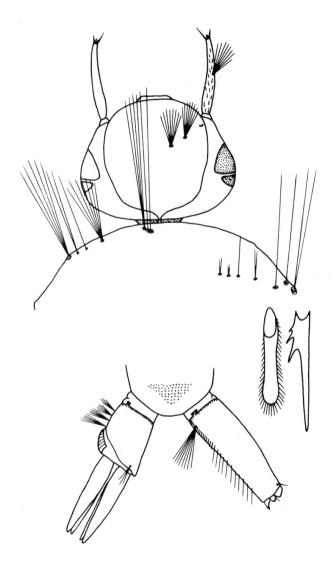

Fig. 66. Larva, *Cs. impatiens*.

Culiseta incidens (Thomson)

Culex incidens Thomson, 1868, Kongl.Sven.Freg.Eug.Resa. 6, Dipt.: 443

(Latin: *incido* = cutting through)

A large mosquito with conspicuously spotted wings and indistinct pale bands on the tarsomeres; wing length 5.5–6 mm.

Female—Proboscis and palps dark with scattered white scales. Pedicels brown, white-scaled on median surface. Scutum with several alternating dark and pale-scaled stripes in median area and with distinct middorso-central spots of pale scales bordered by sparsely scaled posterior half-stripes. Abdominal tergites dark with basal bands of yellowish scales. Tarsomeres with very narrow basal and apical bands, indistinct on forelegs. Wing scales dark, aggregated into distinctive clusters on vein R_s and at bases of R_2, R_3, M_1 and M_2. Crossveins bare, in line with each other.

Larva (Fig. 67)—Antennae short, with few spicules. Head seta 5-C 5 or more branched and shorter than the 2 to 4-branched 6-C. More than 40 slipper-shaped comb scales in a patch (dotted in fig.). Siphon 3×1, a short pecten is followed by a row of setae reaching apical ¼. 1-S many-branched, inserted basally within pecten. Saddle surrounding anal segment. 1-X fine, shorter than saddle.

In 1932, Hearle wrote "This is the most widespread and commonest species in B.C." It is a domestic mosquito and in the 1920s almost every rain water barrel in the Lower Mainland was teeming with its larvae throughout the summer (Hearle 1921). Its larvae are still found in artificial containers, ditches, garden, woodland and polluted pools and in brackish coastal pools where they are often associated with *Ae. togoi* and occasionally with *Ae. dorsalis* larvae. The females hibernate, reappearing in early spring, when partly on account of their large size, they cause consternation out of all proportion to their importance. For reasons that are not clear at present, populations of this species are greater in spring and fall than at the height of summer, although there are several broods each season. Females are not usually aggressive biters and take blood from large mammals more often than from man. I have, however, noticed a temperature effect in the Lower Mainland where this species readily bites humans on warm evenings (above 20°C).

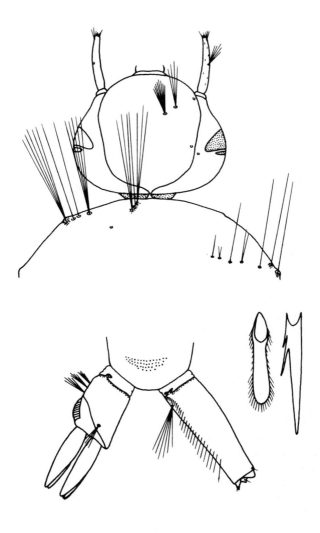

Fig. 67.   Larva, *Cs. incidens*.

Culiseta inornata (Williston)

Culex inornatus Williston, 1893. U.S.Dept.Agr.Divn.Ornith.& Mam.,N.Amer.Fauna 7:253
(Latin: not ornate, probably referring to its lack of striking markings)

A large, drab mosquito with unbanded tarsi; wing length 5–6 mm.

Female—Proboscis and palps dark with scattered pale scales. Pedicels brown, median surface sparsely white-scaled. Scutum with mixed light brown and yellow scales forming indistinct stripes. Abdominal tergites with broad basal bands of yellowish-white scales, widening laterally in many specimens to become continuous from segment to segment. Legs with dark and pale scales. Wings unspotted, scales dark and sparse on all but anterior veins, where some white scales are intermixed. Crossveins close together but not in line.

Larva (Fig. 68)—Antennae short, sparsely spiculate. Head seta 5-C 5 or more branched and shorter than fewer-branched 6-C. More than 40 rounded comb scales in a patch (dotted in fig.). Siphon 3×1, pecten short, followed by a row of setae extending to apical $\frac{1}{4}$. 1-S large, inserted within pecten, near base of siphon. Saddle surrounding anal segment. 1-X as long as saddle, 1 or 2-branched.

This mosquito is widely distributed across the Province, mainly in the south, but nowhere very numerous. Adults seem to prefer the blood of larger mammals to that of man and thus escape notice, even when they are present, although where locally numerous they may seriously pester cattle. Females overwinter in mammal burrows and crevices in rocky ground. They are most commonly observed when emerging from hibernation in early spring, or when attracted to lights. They have been seen flying in weather too cold for almost any other insect, often coming out for a day or two during a fine spell in winter, even when snow is lying. In Utah larvae have been found in ice-covered pools (Nielsen & Rees 1961). In this Province, larvae breed in deep shaded woodland pools, irrigation seepage and polluted and brackish water in the open. In the Lower Mainland, I have found adults mating on the ground at the edge of woodland pools where the larvae were developing. Burton & McLintock

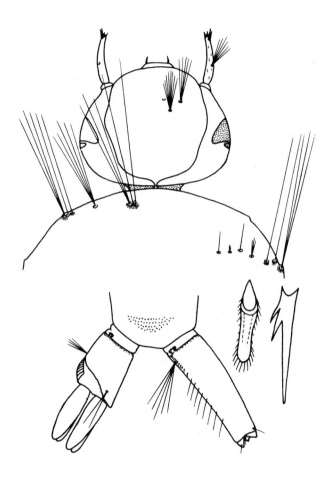

Fig. 68. Larva, *Cs. inornata*.

(1970) considered *inornata* to be the main transmitter of WEE virus in the far north. However, since they rarely bite humans they are not a menace in this respect.

Culiseta morsitans (Theobald)

Culex morsitans Theobald, 1901. Mon.Culic. 2:8
Culex dyari Coquillett, 1902.
(Latin: biting)

A medium to large species, the tarsomeres faintly banded basally; wing length 5–5.5 mm.

Female—Proboscis and palps dark-scaled. Pedicels brown with brown setae on median surface. Scutum brown with yellowish scales toward margins and, in most specimens, an indefinite pair of bare median stripes and posterolateral half-stripes. Abdominal tergites clothed with bronzy-brown scales, scattered yellowish ones forming basal bands in some specimens. Tarsomeres dark with faint narrow basal bands of pale scales. Tibiae and first tarsomeres with a few pale scales apically. Wings dark-scaled, a few white ones at base of C. Crossveins bare and separated by slightly less than length of m-cu. Male genitalia are distinct from *minnesotae*.

Larva (Fig. 69)—Antennae long, curved, spiculate. Head seta 5-C 4 to 5-branched, 6-C 2-branched and much longer than 5-C. 50 or more slipper-shaped comb scales in a patch (dotted in fig.). Siphon about 6×1, a few pecten teeth on basal $\frac{1}{5}$, distal ones widely spaced. 1-S 4 or 5-branched, inserted basally. Anal segment longer than wide, surrounded by saddle. Ventral "brush" of 20 or more many-branched setae.

This mosquito has a fairly northern distribution, and has been taken at a few widely scattered localities in British Columbia. In recent years it has been locally abundant near Vancouver in a peat-bottomed lake and its surrounding pools (Belton 1978). The eggs are laid in rafts on moist ground, just above the water line (Wallis & Whitman 1968). I found no larvae in known breeding sites in 1978 after heavy January frosts. Winter may have been spent in the egg stage as is apparently the case in New York State (Morris *et al.* 1976). Third and fourth instar larvae were, nevertheless, abundant in March when other raft-laying species had just

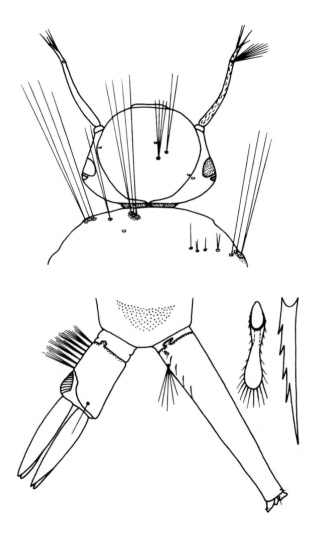

Fig. 69.   Larva, *Cs. morsitans*.

emerged from hibernation and were starting to oviposit. Possibly the larvae overwintered deep in the peat and silt at the bottom of the pools. In the same area, in late June, small swarms of males were seen at sunset flying in an extended figure-of-eight about 2 m above the ground in the leaves and branches of a cascara tree. Females captured in flight or reared from larvae would not take a human blood meal. They feed mainly on birds.

Culiseta minnesotae Barr

Culiseta minnesotae Barr, 1957. Proc.Ent.Soc.Wash. 59:163
(Latin: of Minnesota)

A medium to large mosquito with faintly banded tarsi and abdominal tergites with pale basal and apical bands; wing length 5–5.5 mm.

Female—Proboscis and palps dark-scaled. Pedicels light brown, a few dark scales on mediodorsal surface. Scutum clad in coppery-brown scales with lines of dark setae and small paired patches of silvery scales in front of prescutellar space. Abdominal tergites with basal and apical bands or patches of pale scales (no apical bands in *morsitans*). Hind tarsi with very narrow pale basal bands on segments 2 and 3, and on 1 and 4 in some specimens. Wings brown-scaled, some pale ones on base of C. Male genitalia are distinct from *morsitans*.

Larva—A diagram of this species has not been included. The larvae, none of which have yet been found in the Province, are very similar to *morsitans*. Differences are noted in the following description (from various sources). Antennae long, strongly spiculate. Head seta 5-C 7 to 8-branched (4 to 5 in *morsitans*), 6-C 2 or 3-branched and twice as long as 5-C. Numerous slipper-shaped comb scales in a patch. Siphon 7×1, a very short pecten on basal ¼, distal teeth widely spaced. 1-S inserted basally within pecten. Anal segment longer than wide, surrounded by saddle. Ventral "brush" of 17 or 18 many-branched setae (20 in *morsitans*).

In 1974 Costello (1977) collected two females in a light-trap near Vancouver and so far, these are the only confirmed records from the Province. This species is closely related to *morsitans*, however, and many records of *morsitans* before 1957 may refer to *minnesotae*. Larvae breed in permanent marshes with clumps of sedge and cattail (Wood *et al.* 1979). In Alberta, females were found hibernating under rock piles.

Genus *Mansonia*

Mansonia Blanchard, 1901. C.R.Soc.Biol. 53:1045

Mansonia was named after Sir Patrick Manson who studied the role of mosquitoes in the transmission of malarial and nematode parasites in the 1870's.

Some authorities have resurrected the subgeneric name, *Coquillettidia* Dyar, 1905, for the part of this genus that includes our species, *perturbans*. As the name *Mansonia perturbans* has been used continuously since the 1920's however, I have followed Wood *et al.* (1979) in retaining Blanchard's name.

Only one species of the genus occurs in Canada. The structure and habits of the larvae and pupae of this mosquito set it apart from all others in the country. The siphon of the larva and respiratory "trumpets" of the pupa are modified so that these stages can attach themselves to the underwater stems and roots of plants (mainly cattails, *Typha latifolia,* in British Columbia) which provide all their oxygen requirements. Because the immature stages do not surface for air they are difficult to find and, incidentally, difficult to control with pesticides.

This is the only blunt-ended female in the Province that has a pale band at mid length on the first hind tarsomere. The wing scales are unusually broad.

The eggs are laid in clusters on or above the water surface among the "host" plants. The first instar larvae, which obtain all the oxygen they need by diffusion through the body, swim down and pierce the plant with a specially adapted siphon. Moulting and pupation occur while larvae are attached to the plant. The last larval moult is complicated because the siphon is lost and the pupa has to insert its respiratory "trumpets" into the plant. When the pupa is ready to moult it breaks off the drill-like ends of the "trumpets" and rises to the surface where the adult emerges.

Mansonia perturbans (Walker)

Culex perturbans Walker, 1856. Ins.Saund.Dipt.: 428
(Latin: disturbing)

Fig. 70, wing scales; larval abdomen

A medium sized species with striking tarsal bands, and dusty looking wings, wing length 4–5 mm. Larval siphon adapted to pierce plants.

Female—Proboscis dark with a diffuse broad pale band at mid length. Palps short, dark with a few scattered pale scales. Pedicels brown, a few pale scales on darker median surface. Scutum thinly covered with brownish to pale yellow scales and in most specimens, two longitudinal pale lines on the bare cuticle. Abdominal tergites dark-scaled with pale basolateral patches, joining to form continuous basal bands in some specimens. Legs with mixed light and dark scales; hind tibiae with a pale band near the apex. First tarsomeres with a narrow basal band and a broader one at mid length; remaining segments with very broad basal bands. Wing scales very broad, light and dark mixed.

Larva—Antennae distinctive, very long and curved, 1-A large and many-branched, a pair of short setae inserted beyond it. Head setae 5 & 6-C 6 or more-branched, 6-C longer than 5-C. 8–15 thorn-shaped comb scales in a single ragged row. Siphon unlike that of our other mosquito larvae, short and conical with a serrated tip bearing a stout curved dorsal seta and no pecten (Fig. 70). Anal segment longer than broad, surrounded by saddle.

This species has been found in the Fraser, Okanagan and Kootenay valleys and no doubt will be found elsewhere in the Province. There is one generation a year. The larvae breed in swampy lakeshore with abundant cattails or similar vegetation. They overwinter and can survive extensive periods of freezing (Rademacher 1979). The female is a strong flier and an aggressive biter. Hearle (1926) wrote "No other mosquito that we are acquainted with has such virulent poison. It shows no timidity in attack and is very persistent in entering houses." In 1980 it is still annoying in the evening from late June until September when it enters houses in the Lower Mainland. Fortunately, it does not appear to be present anywhere in the Province in sufficient numbers to become a serious pest. The larval and pupal behaviour make it difficult to control (see genus description) and the adults will have to be kept at bay with screens and repellents.

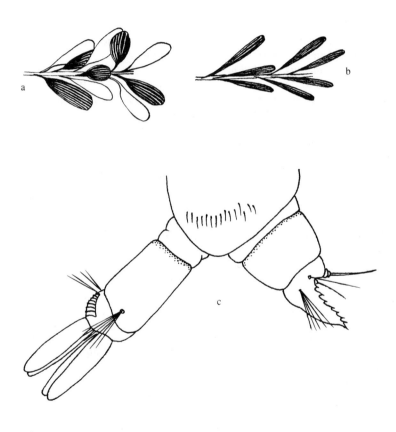

Fig. 70.   a. wing scales, *Mansonia*; b. wing scales, *Aedes*; c. terminal segments of larva, *Ma. perturbans*.

Species to look for

Seven species of mosquitoes that have been found in neighbouring states and provinces may, sooner or later, be collected in British Columbia. Some of them may, in fact, have been collected already but misidentified as similar species. Four species, *punctodes, ventrovittis, peus* and *particeps* have not yet been found in Canada.

Ae. churchillensis Ellis & Brust was discussed with its sibling species, *communis,* on p. 90. The smaller *churchillensis* is found in Alberta and probably occurs in northeastern British Columbia.

Ae. nigromaculis (Ludlow) is a prairie species that has been found in Alberta, close to our eastern border, and probably occurs in the Peace River along with *riparius*. It is included in the keys and cannot easily be confused with other aedines found in the Province.

Ae. punctodes Dyar breeds in coastal salt marshes in Alaska and may breed in similar habitats along our northern coast. Females are indistinguishable from those of *punctor;* in *punctodes* larvae, however, the anal papillae are short and the saddle does not surround the anal segment entirely as it does in *punctor.*

Ae. schizopinax Dyar is found in the Rocky Mountain foothills west of Calgary and in Oregon and Washington. It may be present in mountainous regions in the south of the Province and in the Kootenays. It has been included in the keys.

Ae. ventrovittis Dyar may occur in or near Manning Provincial Park, not many kilometres from where it is found in Chelan Co., northern Washington (Gjullin & Eddy 1972). Both adults and larvae are similar to *impiger* but, according to Bohart & Washino (1978), the pale basal bands on the abdominal tergites are sharply indented or separated medially in *ventrovittis* adults whereas they are of even width in all the *impiger* adults I have examined. The larvae of *ventrovittis* have more widely and unevenly spaced pecten teeth than *impiger.*

Cx. peus Speiser and *Cs. particeps* (Adams) may extend their range into the Province or may already occur here and both have been included in the keys. *Cx. peus* is produced in great numbers in log ponds in Oregon and Washington and should be looked for in the Lower Mainland (Curtis 1967a). *Cs. particeps* has been collected in northwest Washington (Myklebust 1966) and at the southern end of the Alaskan Panhandle (Bickley 1976) and should be looked for in the Gulf Islands and coastal forest.

GLOSSARY

(some definitions apply only to species in British Columbia)

Abdomen—the posterior of three main body divisions, composed of 10 segments, 8 of which are visible in adult mosquitoes.

Acus (pl. aci)—a small sclerite, at or near base of saddle or siphon of some larvae.

Aedine—belonging to the genus *Aedes*.

Anal papillae—translucent tubular appendages, that maintain correct salt and water balance, on anal segment of larva (Fig. 6).

Anal vein (abbr. A)—posterior vein of wing (Fig. 10).

Anopheline—belonging to the genus *Anopheles*.

Antennae—paired segmented sensory organs at front of head.

Apex (adj. apical)—at or near the tip, or an area far from the centre—opp. basal.

Appressed—flattened close to surface.

Autogeny—ability in an adult female to produce eggs without a blood meal.

Band—running transversely or encircling a segment, usually applied to colour pattern—opp. longitudinal stripe.

Basal—close to base or centre of body—opp. apical.

Benthic—at the bottom of a body of water.

Biotic area—an area characterized by a number of particular plants and animals.

Borrow pits—dug-out farm ponds.

C.E.—California encephalitis, a viral disease.

Cercus (pl. cerci)—paired processes at apex of abdomen of adult females, projecting in aedines (Table I).

Clypeal setae—on an anterior sclerite of head, used to distinguish anopheline larvae (Fig. 16).

Comb, comb scales—a patch of spiny scales on abdominal segment VIII, in culicine larvae (Fig. 6).

Costa (abbr. C)—thickened anterior margin of wing (Fig. 10).

Coxa—basal segment of leg (Fig. 11).

Cratis—sclerotised area on anal segment of larva, supporting swimming setae (Fig. 6).

Cubitus (abbr. Cu)—vein of wing (Fig. 10).

Culicine—belonging to the tribe Culicini.

Cuticle—non-cellular outer covering of insect, pale and flexible unless sclerotised.

Cytoplasm (adj.—plasmic)—living contents of a cell, not including nucleus.

Diapause—a period when egg or larval development is arrested, enabling a species to survive the winter.

Distal—same as apical.

Egg raft—a tightly packed cluster of vertically oriented eggs that floats on the surface of water (Table I).

Encephalitis—a disease of the nervous system caused by an insect-borne virus.

Epimeron and episternum—areas on pleuron (side of adult thorax) that are subdivided into several small sclerites, e.g. mesepimeron, katepisternum, etc. (Fig. 7).

Femur—third and thickest segment of leg (Fig. 11).

Generation—complete cycle of egg, larva, pupa, adult.

Genitalia—external reproductive appendages.

Genus (pl. genera)—a group of species having one or more major characters in common.

Gonocoxite—lateral arm of male genitalia (Fig. 13).

Holarctic—distributed in both North America and Eurasia.

Hydrophobic—water repellent.

Hypostigmal area—region below mesothoracic spiracle (Fig. 7).

Instar—one stage in the growth of a larva, separated from other stages by a moult.

Larva—major stage in life cycle, between egg and pupa (Table I).

Lateral stripe—a line of darker scales along edge of scutum in some aedines (Fig. 9).

Media (abbr. M)—vein of wing (Fig. 10).

Median—at or near middle—opp. lateral.

Mesothorax—middle thoracic segment; mes(o)—pertaining to mesothorax, e.g. mesonotum.

Metathorax—hind thoracic segment; met(a)—pertaining to metathorax, e.g. metepimeron.

Moult—to cast old skin before entering a new stage.

Multivoltine—capable of having more than one generation a year.

Notum—dorsal region of thorax.

Occiput—rear of head (Fig. 7).

Oviposit—deposit eggs.

Palmate setae—fan-shaped setae on abdomen of anopheline larvae (Fig. 17).

Palp(s)—paired sensory appendages on either side of proboscis, long in males and in female anophelines (Fig. 7).

Pecten, pecten teeth—a row of thorn-like spines on either side of siphon (Fig. 6).

Pedicel—enlarged segment near base of adult antenna (Fig. 7).

Phytoplankton—microscopic aquatic plants.

Pleuron (pl. pleura)—side of thorax.

Postprocoxal membrane—connects front coxa to katepisternum (Fig. 7), bearing scales in some species.

Proboscis—elongate tubular mouthparts of adult.

Prothorax—anterior thoracic segment; pro- pertaining to prothorax, e.g. procoxal.

Pupa (verb, to pupate)—third stage of life cycle, between larva and adult (Table I).

Radius (abbr. R)—vein of wing (Fig. 10).

Rafts—*see* egg rafts.

Saddle—sclerite on anal segment of larva (Fig. 6).

Scale—a small flattened seta with a microscopic socket.

Sclerite (adj. sclerotised)—a thickened, fairly rigid region of cuticle, bounded by sutures or membranous areas.

Scutellum—curved sclerite behind scutum (Fig. 9).

Scutum—largest dorsal part of adult thorax (Fig. 7).

Segment—a subdivision of the body or of an appendage.

Seta (pl. setae)—a hair-like or bristle-like outgrowth, arising from a socket.

Sibling species—closely related species that could potentially interbreed but are usually reproductively isolated.

Siphon—posterior respiratory tube of larva (Fig. 6).

SLE—St. Louis encephalitis, a viral disease.

Species—a population of simular individuals that breed among themselves, but not with other populations.

Spicule—a minute pointed spine.

Spine—pointed conical outgrowth of cuticle, without a socket.

Spiracle(s)—external paired openings in cuticle for exchange of gases with the tracheae (internal breathing tubes) (Fig. 7).

Sternite—sclerite of sternum or ventral region of abdominal segment.

Synonym—a name that was, or is still, incorrectly, used for a species.

Tarsus—apical 5 segments (tarsomeres) of leg, bearing terminal claws (Fig. 11).

Taxonomic—pertaining to classification.

Tergite—sclerite of tergum or dorsal portion of abdominal segment.

Terminalia—euphimism for genitalia.

Tibia—fourth segment of leg, between femur and tarsus.

Treehole mosquito—a species that develops in water-filled rot cavities of trees.

Univoltine—having only one generation a year.

Vertex—top of head (Fig. 7).

Ventral brush—a row of long swimming setae on anal segment of larva (Fig. 6).

Vector—transmitter of disease.

WEE—Western equine encephalitis, a viral disease.

APPENDIX

SUPPLIERS

Natural history dealers that used to sell mounted insects, shells, fossils and essential supplies for amateur entomologists are, unfortunately, almost extinct. Some of the suppliers listed below may stipulate minimum orders, or require a letter from a school or other offical source. Enthusiasts can receive support from schools colleges, universities or the Provincial Museum if they have any difficulty. Two of the suppliers are in the United States and most purchases over $10 will be subject to duty and sales tax. These firms are included because they are entomological specialists. There are mosquito experts on the staff of AMBI and of Pest Management Group in Vancouver.

American Biological Supply Company (AMBI)
1330 Dillon Heights Ave., Baltimore, MD. 21228, USA.
(Entomological supplies: insect boxes and drawers, vials, pins, collecting kits, nets, labels, aspirators, killing fluid, magnifiers, microscopes, slides, cover glasses, dippers, etc.)

Arbor Scientific Ltd.,
Box 113, Port Credit, Ont.
(General biological Supplies; killing, preserving and mounting fluids, hypodermic syringes, etc.)

Pest Management Group Ltd.,
545 W. 8th St., Vancouver, B.C. V5Z 1C6
($30 \times$ Microscope with illuminator and mosquito control equipment.)

Bioquip Products,
P.O. Box 61, Santa Monica, CA 90406, USA.
(Entomological supplies as above, also mosquito traps and rearing containers.)

Boreal Laboratories,
1820 Mattawa Ave., Mississauga, Ont. L4X 1K6.
(General biological supplies.)

Northwest Laboratories Ltd.,
3581 Shelbourne St., Victoria, B.C. V8P 5L4.
(General biological supplies, also polyvinyl alcohol.)

REFERENCES

AGRICULTURE CANADA. 1972. Planning an Anti-Mosquito Campaign. Can.Dep.Agric., Ottawa, Publ.1495. 15pp.

ARNELL, J. H., and L. T. NIELSEN. 1972. Mosquito studies XXVII. The *varipalpus* group of *Aedes* (*Ochlerotatus*). Contrib.Amer.Entomol.Inst. (8):1–48.

BARBEAU, M. 1953. Haida myths illustrated in argillite carvings. Nat. Mus.of Can. Anthro., Ser. No. 32, Bull. 127, Ottawa.

———— 1957. Haida carvers in argillite. Nat. Mus.of Can. Anthro., Ser. No. 38, Bull. 139, Ottawa.

BARR, A. R. 1958. The mosquitoes of Minnesota (Diptera: Culicidae: Culicinae). Univ.Minn.Agric.Exp.Stn., Tech.Bull. 228. 154 pp.

BELKIN, J. N., and W. A. McDONALD. 1957. A new species of *Aedes* (*Ochlerotatus*) from tree holes in southern Arizona and a discussion of the *varipalpus* complex. Ann. Entomol.Soc.Amer. 50:179–191.

BELTON, P. 1978. The mosquitoes of Burnaby Lake, British Columbia. J.Entomol.Soc.B.C. 75:20–22.

BICKLEY, W. E. 1976. Notes on the distribution of Alaskan mosquitoes. Mosquito Syst. 8(3):232–236.

BODDY, D. W. 1948. An annotated list of the Culicidae of Washington. Pan-Pacif.Entomol. 24(2):85–94.

BOHART, R. M., and R. K. WASHINO. 1978. Mosquitoes of California. 3rd.ed.,Univ.of Calif., Div.Agric.Sci., Publ. 4804. 153pp.

B.C. MOSQUITO ADVISORY COMMITTEE. 1981. British Columbia mosquito control guide. B.C.Min.Agric.and Food, Publ. 81. 14pp.

BRUST, R. A. 1968. Temperature induced intersexes in *Aedes* mosquitoes: comparative study of species from Manitoba. Can.Entomol. 100:879–891.

BRUST, R. A., and R. A. COSTELLO. 1969. Mosquitoes of Manitoba. II. The effect of storage temperature and relative humidity on hatching of eggs of *Aedes vexans* and *Aedes abserratus* (Diptera: Culicidae). Can.Entomol. 101:1285–1291.

BURTON, A. N., and J. McLINTOCK. 1970. Further evidence of W.E. infection in Saskatchewan mammals and birds and in reindeer in northern Canada. Can.Vet.Jour. 11:232–235.

CAMERON, A. E., R. C. TREHERNE, and S. HADWEN. 1917. Doing away with the mosquito pest. Agric.Jour. (B.C. Dep.Agric.) 2:56.

CANNINGS, R. A., and K. M. STUART. 1977. The Dragonflies of British Columbia. B.C.Prov.Mus.Handbk.35. 254pp.

CARPENTER, S. J., and W. J. LA CASSE. 1955. Mosquitoes of North America (north of Mexico). Univ.of Calif. Press, Berkeley, vi + 360pp.

CARPENTER, S. J. and L. T. NIELSEN. 1965. Ovarian cycles and longevity in some univoltine *Aedes* species in the Rocky Mountains of the western United States. Mosq. News 25:127–134.

CHAPMAN, H. C., and A. R. BARR. 1964. *Aedes communis nevadensis,* a new subspecies of mosquito from western North America (Diptera: Culicidae). Mosq. News 24:439–447.

COQUILLETT, D. W. 1904. New North American Diptera. Proc.Entomol.Soc.Wash. 6:166–192.

COSTELLO, R. A. 1977. The first record of *Culiseta silvestris minnesotae* Barr in British Columbia (Diptera: Culicidae). J.Entomol.Soc.B.C. 74:9.

CROSBY, T. 1907. Among the A-koo-me-nums or Flathead Tribe of Indians of the Pacific Coast. Toronto, Briggs. 243pp.

CURTIS, L. C. 1967a. The Mosquitoes of British Columbia. B.C.Prov.Mus.Occasional Paper No. 15. 90pp.

——— 1967b. How To Wage A Mosquito Control Campaign. Can.Dep.Agric., Ottawa, Publ. 936. 14pp.

DANKS, H. V., and P. S. CORBET. 1973. A key to all stages of *Aedes nigripes* and *A. impiger* (Diptera: Culicidae) with a description of first-instar larvae and pupae. Can.Entomol. 105:367–376.

DYAR, H. G. 1904. Notes on the mosquitoes of British Columbia. Proc.Entomol.Soc.Wash. 6:7–14.

———— 1919. Westward extension of the Canadian mosquito fauna. Insecutor Inscit.Menstr. 7:11–13.

———— 1920. The mosquitoes of British Columbia and the Yukon Territory, Canada (Diptera: Culicidae). Insecutor Inscit.Menstr. 8:165–173.

ELLIS, R. A., and R. A. BRUST. 1973. Sibling species delimitation in the *Aedes communis* (Degeer) aggregate (Diptera: Culicidae). Can.J.Zool. 51:915–959.

FREEMAN, T. N. 1952. Interim report of the distribution of the mosquitoes obtained in the Northern Insect Survey. Defense Research Board, Ottawa. Tech.Rep.1, 2pp.

GIBSON, A. 1931. Mosquito suppression in Canada in 1930. Proc.New Jers. Mosq.Exterm.Ass. 18:1–16.

———— 1933. Mosquito suppression work in Canada in 1932. Proc.New Jers.Mosq.Exterm.Ass. 20:92–102.

———— 1935. Mosquito suppression work in Canada in 1934. Proc.New Jers.Mosq.Exterm.Ass. 22:77–92.

———— 1937. Mosquito suppression work in Canada in 1936. Proc.New Jers.Mosq.Exterm.Ass. 24:96–108.

GILLESPIE, B. I. 1978. The effect of water temperature on oviposition and other aspects of the life history of *Aedes aegypti* (L.) and *Culex pipiens* L. M.Sc.Thesis, Simon Fraser Univ., Burnaby, B.C.

GJULLIN, C. M., and G. W. EDDY. 1972. The mosquitoes of the northwestern United States. U.S.Dep.Agric.Tech.Bull. No. 1447. 111pp.

GJULLIN, C. M., R. I. SAILER, A. STONE, and B. V. TRAVIS. 1961. The Mosquitoes of Alaska. U.S.Dep.Agric.,Agric. Handbk. 182. 98pp.

GRAHAM, P. 1969. Observations on the biology of adult female mosquitoes (Diptera: Culicidae) at George Lake, Alberta, Canada. Quaest.Entomol. 5:309–339.

HADWEN, S. 1915. A note on the occurrence and significance of Anophelinae in British Columbia. Proc.Entomol.Soc.B.C. 5:81–82.

HAPPOLD, D. C. 1965. Mosquito ecology in central Alberta. II Adult populations and activities. Can.J.Zool. 48:821–846.

HAYLES, L. B., H. H. WEEGAR, J. O. IVERSON, and J. McLIN-TOCK. 1979. Overwintering sites of adult mosquitoes in Saskatchewan. Mosq.News 39:117–120.

HEARLE, E., 1920. Notes on some mosquitoes new to Canada. Can.Entomol. 52:114–116.

——— 1921. The importance of mosquitoes, with notes on some British Columbia species. Proc.Entomol.Soc.B.C. 13 & 15:132–135.

——— 1922. An aerial survey of mosquito breeding places. Agric.Gaz.Can. 9:191–195.

——— 1923a. A new mosquito from British Columbia (Culicidae, Diptera). Can.Entomol. 55:4–5.

——— 1923b. Notes on two mosquitoes from British Columbia (Culicidae, Diptera). Can.Entomol. 55:265–266.

——— 1926. The mosquitoes of the Lower Fraser Valley, British Columbia, and their control. Nat.Res. Counc.Can.,Rep. 17. 94pp.

——— 1927a. List of mosquitoes of British Columbia. Proc.Entomol.Soc.B.C. 24:11–19.

——— 1927b. Mosquito control activities in western Canada. Entomol.Soc.Ont.Ann.Rep. 58:45–50.

——— 1927c. A new Canadian mosquito. Can.Entomol. 59:101–103.

——— 1927d. Notes on the occurrence of *Aedes* (*Ochlerotatus*) *nearcticus* Dyar in the Rocky Mountains Park, Alberta (Culicidae, Diptera). Can.Entomol. 59:61–63.

HEARLE, E. 1929. The life history of *Aedes flavescens* Müller. Trans.R.Soc.Can.,3rd Ser. 23:85–101.

———— 1932. Notes on the more important mosquitoes of Western Canada. Proc.New Jers.Mosq.Exterm.Ass. 19:7–15.

HEARLE, E. and C. R. TWINN. 1928. Mosquito control in Canada. Can.Dep.Agric., Ottawa, Entomol.Branch Circular 62. 4pp.

HOCKING, B. 1953. The intrinsic range and speed of flight of insects. Trans.R.Entomol.Soc.Lond. 104:223–345.

HOCKING, B., W. R. RICHARDS, and C. R. TWINN. 1950. Observations on the bionomics of some northern mosquito species (Culicidae: Diptera). Can.J.Res., D, 28:58–80.

HORSFALL, W. R., W. F. HARLAND, L. J. MORETTI, and J. R. LARSEN. 1973. Bionomics and embryology of the inland floodwater mosquito, *Aedes vexans*. Univ.of Illinois Press, Urbana. 211pp.

HOWARD, L. O. 1900. Notes on mosquitoes of the United States, U.S.D.A., Div.Entomol., Bull. 25. 70pp.

HUDSON, J. E. 1978. Canada's national mosquito? Mass-resting of *Anopheles earlei* (Diptera: Culicidae) females in a beaver lodge in Alberta. Can.Entomol. 110:1345–1346.

JAMES, H. G. 1961. Some predators of *Aedes stimulans* (Walk.) and *Aedes trichurus* (Dyar) (Diptera: Culicidae) in woodland pools. Can.J.Zool. 39:533–540.

JAMES, H. G., G. WISHART, R. E. BELLAMY, M. MAW, and P. BELTON. 1969. An annotated list of mosquitoes of southeastern Ontario. Proc.Entomol.Soc.Ont. 100:200–230.

JONES, M. D. R., and S. J. GUBBINS. 1978. Changes in the circadian flight activity of the mosquito, *Anopheles gambiae,* in relation to insemination, feeding and oviposition. Physiol.Entomol. 3:213–220.

KALPAGE, K. S. P., and R. A. BRUST. 1968. Mosquitoes of Manitoba. I. Descriptions and a key to *Aedes* eggs (Diptera: Culicidae). Can.J.Zool. 46:699–718.

KNAB, F. 1907. Mosquitoes as flower visitors. J.N.Y.Entomol.Soc. 15:215–219.

KNIGHT, K. L. 1951. The *Aedes* (*Ochlerotatus*) *punctor* subgroup in North America (Diptera, Culicidae). Ann.Entomol.Soc.Am. 44:87–99.

KNIGHT, K. L., and A. STONE. 1977. A catalog of the mosquitoes of the world (Diptera: Culicidae). Entomol.Soc.Am. (Thomas Say Found.), Wash.6. 611pp.

LaCASSE, W. J., and S YAMAGUTI. 1950. Mosquito fauna of Japan and Korea. Off.Surgeon, 8th U.S. Army, Kyoto, Honshu. 268pp.

LAMB, W. K. (Ed.) 1960. Simon Fraser, Letters and Journals, 1806–1808. McMillan, Canada.

LINDSAY, I. S., and J. M. MCANDLESS. 1978. Permethrin-treated jackets versus repellent-treated jackets and hoods for personal protection against blackflies and mosquitoes. Mosq.News 38:350–356.

LORD, J. K. 1866. A naturalist in Vancouver Island and British Columbia. Vol.2. London. 375pp.

MAIL, A. 1934. The mosquitoes of Montana. Bull.Mont.Agric.Exp.Stn. 288. 72pp.

MARTIN, J. E. H. 1977. Collecting, Preparing and Preserving Insects, Mites and Spiders. Can.Dep.Agric., Res.Branch,Publ. 1643. 182pp.

MCLINTOCK, J., A. N. BURTON, J. A. MCKIEL, and R. R. HALL. 1970. Known mosquito hosts of W.E. virus in Saskatchewan. J.Med.Entomol. 7:446–454.

MORGANTE, O., and J. A. SHEMANCHUK. 1975. Results of a five year study on the ecology and epidemiology of W.E. in Alberta. Proc.Alta.Mosq.Ab.Symp. 1975:31–38.

MORRIS, C. D., R. H. ZIMMERMAN, and L. A. MAGNARELLI. 1976. The bionomics of *Culiseta melanura* and *Culiseta morsitans dyari* in Central New York State (Diptera: Culicidae). Ann.Entomol.Soc.Am. 69:101–105.

MUNRO, J. A., and I. McT. COWAN. 1947. A Review of The Bird Fauna of British Columbia. B.C.Prov.Mus., Spec.Publ.2. 285pp.

MYKLEBUST, R. J. 1966. Distribution of mosquitoes and chaoborids in Washington State, by Counties. Mosq.News 25:515–519.

NIELSEN, L. T., and D. M. REES. 1961. An identification guide to the mosquitoes of Utah. Univ.Utah Biol.Ser. 12(3):1–58.

OUTRAM, I. 1973. Insects in the art and myths of the northwest coast Indians. Bull.Entomol.Soc.Can. 5:20–26.

RADEMACHER, R. E. 1979. Studies of overwintering larvae of *Coquillettidia perturbans* mosquitoes in Minnesota. Mosq.News 39:135–136.

RALEY, G. H. 1937. A monograph of the totem poles in Stanley Park. Vancouver, B.C. 24pp.

REINERT, J. F. 1975. Abbreviations of mosquito generic names. Mosq.News 7:105–110.

REMPEL, J. G. 1950. A guide to the mosquito larvae of western Canada. Can.J.Res., D. 28:207–248.

RICHARDS, C. S. 1956. *Aedes melanimon* Dyar and related species. Can.Entomol. 88:261–269.

SHEMANCHUK, J. A., A. E. R. DOWNE, and L. BURGESS. 1963. Hosts of mosquitoes (Diptera: Culicidae) from the irrigated areas of Alberta. Mosq.News 23:336–341.

SHEMANCHUK, J. A., and O. MORGANTE. 1967. Isolation of W.E. virus from mosquitoes in Alberta. Can.J.Microbiol. 14:1–5.

SERVICE, M. W. 1976. Mosquito ecology, field sampling methods. John Wiley, London. 583pp.

SIEBERT, E., and W. FORMAN. 1969. North American Indian Art. Masks, amulets, wood carvings and ceremonial dress from the north-west coast. Paul Hamlyn, London. 43pp.

STEWART, H. 1979. Looking at Indian Art of the Northwest Coast. Douglas & McIntyre, Victoria. 111pp.

TWINN, C. R. 1941. Mosquito control in Canada. Can.Dep.Agric.,Ent.Div., Publ.719,Circ.172. 4pp.

———— 1949. Mosquitoes and mosquito control in Canada. Mosq.News 9:35–41.

TWINN, C. R., B. HOCKING, W. C. MCDUFFIE, and H. F. CROSS. 1948. A preliminary account of the biting flies at Churchill, Manitoba. Can.J.Res.,D. 26:334–357.

TWINN, C. R., and D. G. PETERSON. 1955. Control of mosquitoes in Canada. Can.Dep.Agric.,Entomol.Div.,Publ.936. 14pp.

VOCKEROTH, J. R. 1954. Notes on Northern Species of *Aedes*, with descriptions of two new species (Diptera, Culicidae). Can.Entomol. 86:109–116.

WALLIS, R. C., and L. WHITMAN. 1968. Oviposition of *Culiseta morsitans* (Theobald) and comments on the life cycle of the American form. Mosq.News 28:198–200.

WASHINO, R. K., and F. SHAD-DEL. 1969. Autogeny in *Culex peus* Speiser. Mosq.News 29:494–495.

WESENBERG-LUND, C. 1921. Contributions on the biology of the Danish Culicidae. A. F. Host & Son, Copenhagen. 210pp.

WEST, A. S. 1963. Past achievements, current activities and contributions and a view to the future on research on and control of mosquitoes in Canada. Proc.New Jers.Mosq.Exterm.Ass. 50:86–107.

WOOD, D. M. 1977. Notes on the identities of some common nearctic *Aedes* mosquitoes (Diptera, Culicidae). Mosq.News 37:71–81.

WOOD, D. M., P. T. DANG, and R. A. ELLIS. 1979. The mosquitoes of Canada. Diptera: Culicidae. Can.Dep.Agric., Res.Branch, Publ.1686. 390pp.

INDEX TO SPECIES TREATED

(Other names and synonyms shown in italics)

ALSO IN THIS SERIES

* No longer in print.

For more information about these and other publications of the British Columbia Provincial Museum write or telephone:

PUBLICATIONS
British Columbia Provincial Museum
Victoria, British Columbia
V8V 1X4

Phone (604) 387-3701 M50-273